WELCOME!

Quiet Time is a special time that you set aside each day to read God's Word and get to know Him better. It is also an important part of Olympians, a fun Bible centered program for kids just like you in grades 1-6! CHALLENGERS (GRADES 1-2), CONQUERORS (GRADES 3-4), and CHAMPIONS (GRADES 5-6). Just like Olympic athletes train to be the very best they can be, your Olympian coaches will help train you to be the best you can be for Jesus! The goal is to please Jesus in everything we say, do and think!

That is what Olympians is all about!

What you can look forward to:

Olympians will be the highlight of your week!

Each Olympians meeting begins with a fantastic kick-off followed by fun songs, exciting games, a Bible lesson to help you grow, plus so much more!

Your Olympian Coach will help you learn about the Bible, answer your questions, pray for your needs and have a fun time with you as well!

Speaking of fun, wait until you see the Big O-vent game time! It is always a blast with lots of crazy games for you to enjoy!

On top of everything else, you will make some great friends at Olympians!

You won't want to miss out on the great times waiting for you at Olympians!

Ready to Get Started?

It's easy to become a member of Olympians. All you need to do is complete the simple steps listed below. Every time you finish one step, you get a sticker for the inside cover of this book! After you collect all the membership stickers to get your membership patch, you can start collecting even more cool stickers for the Bronze, Silver and Gold levels!

MEMBERSHIP REQUIREMENTS:

1. ATTEND OLYMPIANS FOR THREE WEEKS

2. RECITE THE FOLLOWING PLEDGES:

AMERICAN FLAG:
I pledge allegiance to the flag of the United States of America and to the republic for which it stands; one nation, under God, indivisible with liberty and justice for all.

CANADIANS:
Memorize "Oh, Canada."

CHRISTIAN FLAG:
I pledge allegiance to the Christian flag and to the Savior for whose Kingdom it stands; One Savior, crucified, risen and coming again, with life and liberty for all who believe.

BIBLE:
I pledge allegiance to the Bible, God's Holy Word. I will make it a Lamp unto my feet and a light unto my path; I will hide its words in my heart that I might not sin against God.

CHURCH:
I pledge allegiance to my Church, and to my Lord upon whom it is built. I will love my Pastor, and all the members; and will faithfully support my church with my attendance, money, service and prayers.

3. RECITE THE OLYMPIAN MOTTO:

"I press toward the mark for the prize of the high calling of God in Christ Jesus." Philippians 3:14

4. RECITE THE OLYMPIAN SONG:

Sometimes, Jesus, it is hard to follow You, for I want to do what I want to do. But when the Devil tempts me to stray, Oh this is what I'll say...

I'll raise my torch up to the sky, I'll fly my banner way up high, I'll follow Jesus right behind, I will run the race.

I'll be a Champion for my Lord, I'll conquer temptation with His Word. I'll challenge all those who have never known His grace, to accept God's gift by faith.

What's the next step?

After you earn your membership, there are three levels to get you from the starting line to the finish line in the Olympian race (Bronze, Silver, and Gold). Each time you complete a level you can earn a cool Olympian pin! (You can earn a total of 18 different pins over six years!)

Here is a picture of what the sticker sheet looks like in the front of your book!

As you finish the Bronze, Silver and Gold levels, you will be able to receive some very nice awards to recognize your hard work! You can find these on the next page!

AWARDS You May Win!

Your coaches and parents want you to know how proud they are of all your hard work. These awards are great reminders of the most important part of being an Olympian – what you have learned about Jesus and the Bible!

AWARD PINS - You can collect three per year! You can earn a total of 18 different pins over six years!

AWARD BOX - Display all the awards you earn in a year. Put your membership patch, medal, and pins in this clear frame and hang it in your room!

CERTIFICATES - Show your friends and family what you have done at Olympians with these colorful certificates. Hang them on the refrigerator for all to see!

MEDALS - At the end of each year's race, you can receive a medal for the highest level you finished that year – Bronze, Silver or Gold!

TROPHIES - Qualify to receive one of the best Olympian awards by finishing the Gold level after 2, 4, or 6 years. The Steadfast Trophy is the highest award you can earn for completing the Gold level after six years in Olympians.

Get running and see how far you can go with God this year!

Christian Service Activities

The following is a list of Christian Service Activities to help you learn how to serve God by serving others. A more detailed explanation of each activity is available in the Word of Life Olympian Christian Service Manual on Teacher Source (teachersource.wol.org).

INDIVIDUAL

Christian Service Opportunities

Encouragement Ministry Opportunities

ICS - 1 Encouragement Cards
ICS - 2 Get Well Card
ICS - 3 Giving Thanks
ICS - 4 Helping Hands At Home
ICS - 5 Ministry Of Helps
ICS - 6 Ministry To College Student
ICS - 7 Ministry To Elderly
ICS - 8 Missionary Letter
ICS - 9 Pray For An Adult
ICS - 10 Pray With A Friend
ICS - 11 Telephone Ministry
ICS - 12 Thank You Letter

Church or Evangelistic Opportunities

ICS - 13 Absentee Visitation
ICS - 14 Create A Tract
ICS - 15 Evangelistic Highlight
ICS - 16 Family Devotions
ICS - 17 Gospel Tracts
ICS - 18 Help A Sunday School Teacher
ICS - 19 Help Church Secretary
ICS - 20 Help In The Nursery
ICS - 21 Invite A Friend
ICS - 22 Pen Pal
ICS - 23 Prayer Partner Card
ICS - 24 Puppet Ministry
ICS - 25 Servant's Heart
ICS - 26 Special Music
ICS - 27 Tell A Friend
ICS - 28 Testimony By Olympian
ICS - 29 Visitation
ICS - 30 Testimony By Leader Or Parent

GROUP

Christian Service Opportunities

Encouragement Ministry Opportunities

GCS - 1 Boxes Of Blessing
GCS - 2 Church Clean-up
GCS - 3 Clean & Decorate Olymp. Rm.
GCS - 4 Food Pantry
GCS - 5 Flower Garden
GCS - 6 Get Well Cards
GCS - 7 Ministry of Helps
GCS - 8 Pastor's Testimony
GCS - 9 Pray For Our Country
GCS - 10 Sharing From Plants
GCS - 11 Thank You Letters

Church or Evangelistic Opportunities

GCS - 12 Christmas Or Holiday Caroling
GCS - 13 Drama Team
GCS - 14 Live Nativity
GCS - 15 Missionary Project
GCS - 16 Music Ministry
GCS - 17 Parade Float
GCS - 18 Project Prayer
GCS - 19 Puppet Ministry
GCS - 20 Retirement Home Service
GCS - 21 Senior Citizens Group
GCS - 22 Tract Blitz
GCS - 23 Visit Shut-Ins
GCS - 24 Youth Emphasis Service

POWER UP!!

Challenger

HAD YOUR QUIET TIME today?

Jump-start Your Day!

QT

Olympians

Fueled by The Lord God Almighty

365 days

1yr

Daily Devotional

Holy Thirst Quencher

Spiritual Fuel

GRADES 1-2

WORD OF LIFE

LOCAL CHURCH MINISTRIES

Quiet Time

One year daily devotional for children in grades 1-2

Published by Word of Life Local Church Ministries
A division of Word of Life Fellowship, Inc.
Don Lough - Executive Director
Jack Wyrtzen & Harry Bollback - Founders
Ric Garland - VP of Local Church Ministries

USA
P.O. Box 600
Schroon Lake, NY 12870
1-888-932-5827
talk@wol.org

Canada
RR#8
Owen Sound ON N4K 5W4
1-800-461-3503
LCM@wol.ca

Web Address: www.wol.org

Publisher's Acknowledgements
Writers and Contributors: Jennifer Huntington, Debbie Shrewsberry, Lisa Reichard
Editor: Lisa Reichard
Curriculum Manager: Don Reichard
Design and layout: Sally Robison

ISBN – 978-1-935475-26-2
Printed in the United States of America

God loves you and wants to spend time with you!

Quiet Time is a special time that you set aside each day to read God's Word, to get to know Him better, and to learn how He wants you to live. During this time, God speaks to you through His Holy Word, the Bible, and you speak to God through prayer. What an adventure! As a Christian, spending this time everyday is very important for you to grow closer to God.

This Quiet Time will help you have a special time each day with the Lord. This booklet is divided into two sections: *A Personal Prayer Diary* section where you can write prayer requests to remind yourself to pray for people that you care about and things that are happening and the *Quiet Time Activity Pages* where activities are written from the Bible verses for each day of the year to challenge you to understand the truths from God's Word.

All Word of Life Quiet Times use the same Scriptures for the week. This makes it easier for your whole family to discuss the passages together.

Meet the Challenger friends.

Here are some new friends that you will get to know this year.
They will help and encourage you daily as you spend time with God.

A Note to Parents

This Quiet Time is a great opportunity for you to have fun together with your child. Here are some tips to help your child with the Quiet Time.

- Sit down at a prescribed time each day.
- Gather supplies needed for activities.
- Use the Bible to look up references together.
- Talk through the activity and personal application.
- Encourage your child to use the prayer suggestions in the Pray section and occasionally pray with them.
- Complete the week by documenting how many days were completed and writing an encouraging note.

Your Daily Quiet Time

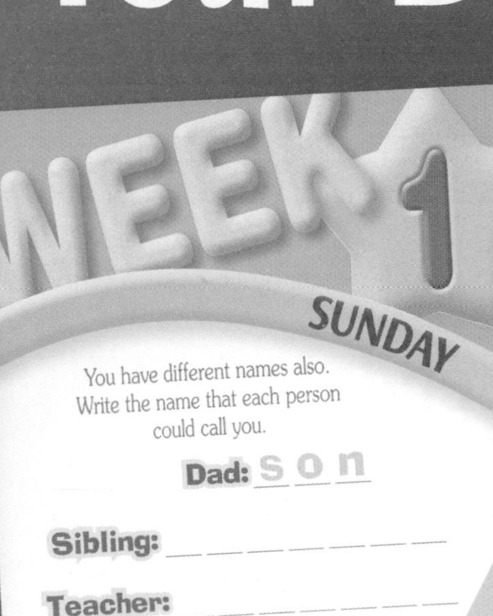

SUNDAY John 1:1

You have different names also. Write the name that each person could call you.

Dad: S o n

Sibling: ____________

Teacher: ____________

Coach: ____________

Classmate: ____________

Student
Friend
Brother
Player

Another name for Jesus is the Word.

Pray Thank God for your name.

MONDAY John 1:10

When Jesus was born people did not recognize Him as God's Son.

Can you recognize these shadows? Draw a line to connect the shadows to the correct word.

dinosaur

robot

house

cat

tiger

Pray Tell God you recognize His Son is Jesus.

TUESDAY John 1:14

Jesus became like a human so He could live here on earth with us. But He was still God.

When you put on a costume you change the way you look, but not who you are. Connect the costume to the name.

Superman

Cinderella

football player

rabbit

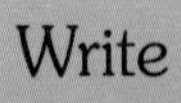

Pray Thank Jesus for coming down to earth to be born as a baby.

10

Begin the week by reading the cartoon featuring your Challenger Friends. This will give you a hint about what you will learn that week.

Each day, read the Daily Scripture Passage in your Bible.

Complete the activity for the day.

Use the Pray statement to guide you as you pray each day.

Write down your prayer requests in your diary and spend time talking to God in prayer.

Things I need for my Quiet Time:

My Bible

My Quiet Time

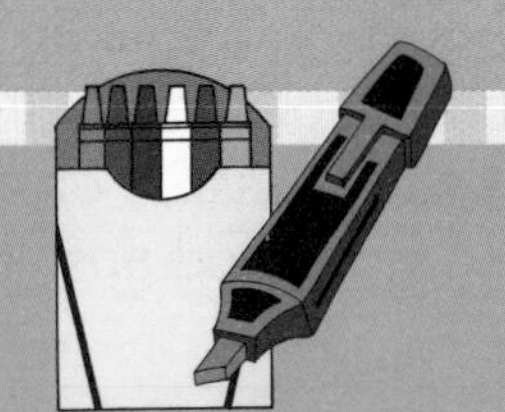

Crayons or Markers

A Quiet Place

My Personal Prayer Diary

Spending time with God in Prayer

Keeping a Personal Prayer Diary is a great way to remind yourself to pray for specific people and things. It also reminds you to thank God and to tell others when He answers your prayers.

Your prayer time should include praying for friends and family. Especially pray for those who don't know Christ as their Savior.

You should also pray for your Christian friends, your relatives and yourself. Pray that you will grow in your Christian life and become what God wants you to be.

Get to know missionaries who serve the Lord in your area or around the world. Ask them for specific prayer requests. Write these on your prayer pages.

Much of your prayer time should be used thanking and praising God. Tell God that you are thankful for your salvation, parents, home, friends, and answers to prayers. You should praise God for His beautiful creation, His holiness and His greatness.

Some prayer time should include asking God to meet needs such as clothing, food or maybe a job for your dad. Maybe you could ask God to help you be more obedient. You must be careful not to be selfish and ask for things that you want only for you. As you are obedient to God, He will care for your needs.

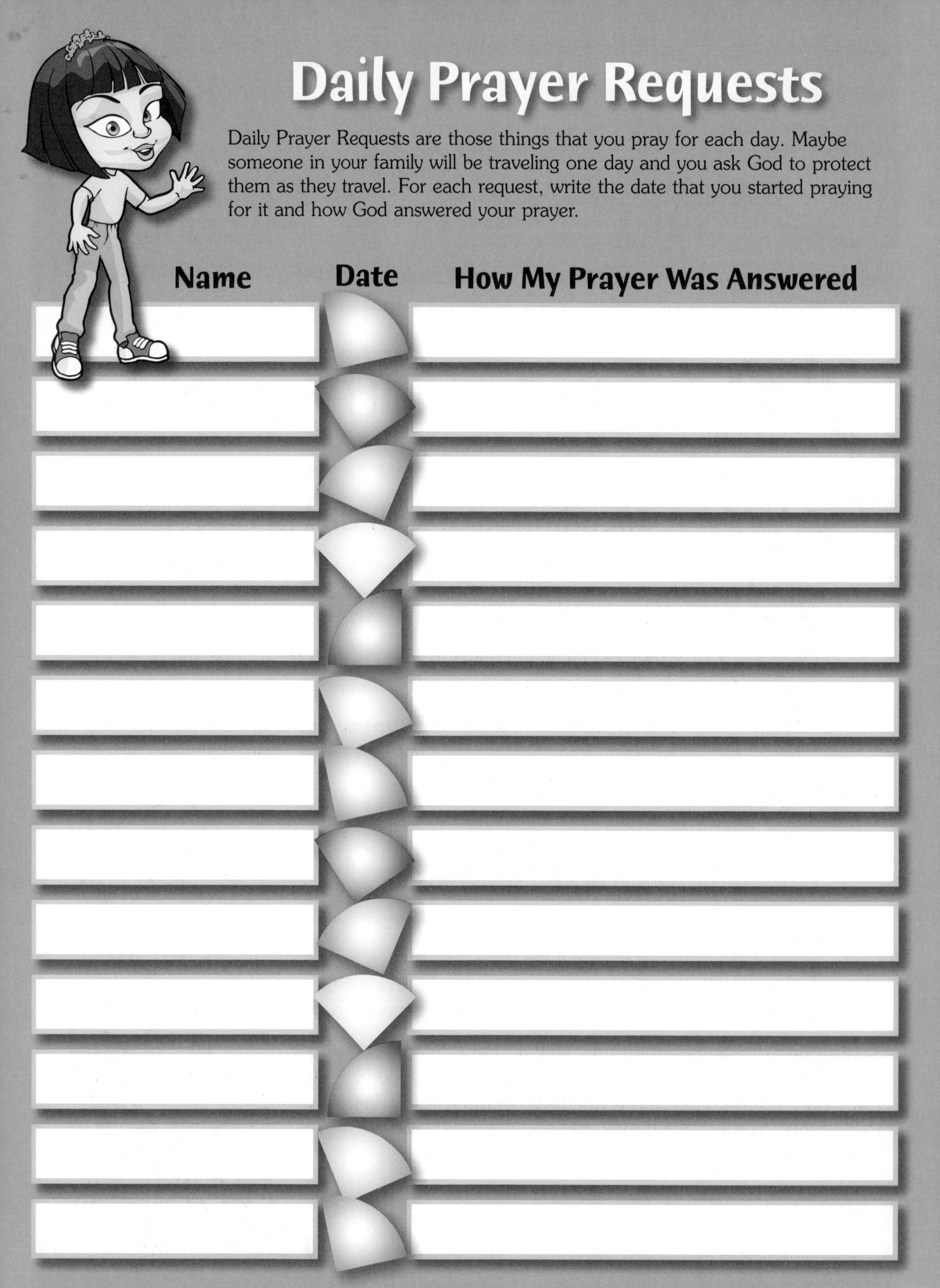

Daily Prayer Requests

Daily Prayer Requests are those things that you pray for each day. Maybe someone in your family will be traveling one day and you ask God to protect them as they travel. For each request, write the date that you started praying for it and how God answered your prayer.

Name	Date	How My Prayer Was Answered

Daily Prayer Requests

Name	Date	How My Prayer Was Answered

Daily Prayer Requests

Name	Date	How My Prayer Was Answered

SUNDAY–family + friends

Name	Date	How My Prayer Was Answered

Missionaries + Church Leaders

Name	Date	How My Prayer Was Answered

I thank God for...	I praise God for...

MONDAY–family + friends

Name	Date	How My Prayer Was Answered

Missionaries + Church Leaders

Name	Date	How My Prayer Was Answered

I thank God for...	I praise God for...

TUESDAY–family + friends

Name	Date	How My Prayer Was Answered

Missionaries + Church Leaders

Name	Date	How My Prayer Was Answered

I thank God for...	I praise God for...

WEDNESDAY–family + friends

Name	Date	How My Prayer Was Answered

MISSIONARIES + CHURCH LEADERS

Name	Date	How My Prayer Was Answered

I THANK GOD FOR...	I PRAISE GOD FOR...

THURSDAY–family + friends

Name	Date	How My Prayer Was Answered

Missionaries + Church Leaders

Name	Date	How My Prayer Was Answered

I thank God for...	I praise God for...

FRIDAY–family + friends

Name	Date	How My Prayer Was Answered

Missionaries + Church Leaders

I thank God for...	I praise God for...

SATURDAY–family + friends

Name	Date	How My Prayer Was Answered

Missionaries + Church Leaders

Name	Date	How My Prayer Was Answered

I thank God for...	I praise God for...

SUNDAY Psalm 104:10-11

Color God's beautiful creation that He cares for.

Pray **Praise God for the weather He has given you today.**

What a wonderful reminder that God is in control of everything that happens on earth. It is by His powerful hands that rivers flow giving drink to the wild animals, that rain comes from the sky, that the sun rises and sets, and that crops grow in the fields.

MONDAY Psalm 104:18, 22-23

God designed the earth. It is He Who created the mountains where the goats live. It is God who planned for man to work during the day. The things of nature didn't happen; they were planned by God Who reigns over all the earth.

How did the things in nature come to be? Color the Xs to find the answer.

XXXGODXXXXPLANNEDX
XXXANDXXXXMADEXXX
XXXEVERYTHINGXXXXXX

Pray **Praise God for the wonderful world He made.**

TUESDAY Psalm 104:33-34

Take time, as this psalmist did, to think about God's power and how He created the world. You will want to join the psalmist and sing praise to God. He is an awesome God.

Look at the picture of the children praising God through song. Can you find the hidden musical notes? Circle them, then write the number you found in the box.

Pray **Praise God by singing your favorite praise song.**

WEDNESDAY Psalm 105:1-2

You should tell everyone about all the things God has done and does. Tell someone how God created the earth. Tell how He sends the rain even now. Tell of all His wonderful works.

Can you think of a wonderful thing God has done that you can share with someone? Draw a picture showing the wonderful thing God has done.

God has done this wonderful thing.

Pray Praise God for being wonderful.

THURSDAY Psalm 105:14

God is in control. When God's people first came into the land of Canaan, it was God who protected them and did not allow the kings of the land to attack them.

Write the first letter of each picture to complete the sentence.

God

_ _ _ _ _ _ _ _

His people.

Pray Thank God for protecting you.

FRIDAY Psalm 105:26

God chose and sent Moses and Aaron to be His "spokesmen" to Pharaoh when the Egyptians were keeping the Israelites as slaves.

Anyone can be used by God to show His power—even you. When you do something that pleases God, it shows Him to others around you and gives Him glory. Circle something you could do today.

TELL SOMEONE ABOUT JESUS

SHARE YOUR FAVORITE TOY

READ THE BIBLE TO SOMEONE

HOLD THE DOOR FOR SOMEONE AT THE STORE

HELP SOMEONE WITH A CHORE

INVITE SOMEONE TO CHURCH

Pray Ask God to help you do things to please Him.

SATURDAY Psalm 105:37

The psalmist remembers all the powerful things God did. It was God who brought the Israelites out of Egypt with silver and gold in their hands.

Look through this psalm and find all the things God did. Write the correct vowels on the lines.

(Verse 16)
God c_ll_d for a famine.

(Verse 28)
God s_nt darkness.

(Verse 34)
God sp_k_ and locust came.

(Verse 41)
God _p_n_d the rock.

Pray Thank God for all the awesome things He has done.

COMMENT CORNER

Parent or Leader, circle a comment and/or write your own.

You can do it

God loves you!

Nice job!

We're proud of you!

Keep it up

WOW!

DAYS COMPLETED

WEEK 2
"Mighty + Just + Loving + Kind+ Good = GOD"
Reading the Psalms is an excellent way to discover Who God is and what to praise Him for.
Who have you learned God is as you read the Psalms?
He is Mighty.
Just.
Always good.
Full of loving-kindness.
SUNDAY Psalm 106:1
God is so good. Draw or write one thing that God has given to you.
God will always love you. Praise Him and thank Him for that.
Pray
Tell God thank you for loving you.
MONDAY Psalm 106:25-26, 29
The Israelites would not listen to God and obey His commands. God is just. He always does what is right. He had to punish their disobedience because it is right to punish those who break His rules.
Put an X next to the actions that would be disobeying God. God calls disobedience sin.
___ Yelling "I hate you." at your brother or sister.
___ Sharing your lunch with a friend.
___ Taking a piece of candy from the store.
___ Praying to God.
___ Not cleaning your room when mom tells you to.
Pray
Ask God to help you obey His Word.
TUESDAY Psalm 106:44-45
When the people of Israel called out to God, He heard them and answered their cry for help.
God loves you. He wants to share His loving-kindness with you. He wants to rescue you from the punishment of sin. To learn more, talk to your parent or an adult at church. Write your name on the line and color the hearts.
Pray
Thank God for His loving-kindness.

WEDNESDAY Psalm 107:1-2

You are commanded to tell others how good and loving God is.

Whom can you tell today about what God has done for you? Write that person's name on the line and color the star when you have told them.

____

(person's name)

Pray Ask God to help you tell others about Him.

THURSDAY Psalm 107:32

This verse is a reminder to go to church to praise God with other Christians.

Put an X on the calendar next to the days you go to church.

SUNDAY	MONDAY	TUESDAY	WEDNESDAY	THURSDAY	FRIDAY	SATURDAY

Pray Tell God thank you for your church.

FRIDAY Psalm 107:33-36

Wisdom comes from reading the Bible, doing what God says, and loving Him.

Write the vowels in the correct blanks to read the sentence.

R_ _d y_ _r B_bl_.
2 1 4 5 3 2

D_ wh_t G_d s_ys.
4 1 4 1

L_v_ the L_rd.
4 2 4

A=1 E=2 I=3 O=4 U=5

Pray Tell God thank you for His Word, the Bible.

SATURDAY Psalm 108:4

God's loving-kindness is greater than you can imagine.

Underline the great group. Circle the greater group. Draw a square around the greatest group of Bibles. Remember God is the greatest and His Word is truth.

Pray Tell God thank you for being the greatest.

COMMENT CORNER Parent or Leader, circle a comment and/or write your own.

You're special | You can do it | God loves you! | Nice job! | We're proud of you! | Keep it up | WOW!

DAYS COMPLETED

WEEK 3

"Worthy of all Praise"

SUNDAY Psalm 114:8

Hold your book in front of a mirror and see what the message says. Write the message on the line.

____

God is great.

Pray Praise God for being so powerful.

MONDAY Psalm 115:1

All glory belongs to God. If you have a talent, God gave you that ability. When someone praises you for your talent, thank them for their compliment AND thank God for giving you the talent. Give Him the praise for who you are and what you can do.

Draw a picture of what you do well and praise God for it. Complete the sentence.

Thank you God that I can ______________________.

Pray Praise God for the things you do well.

TUESDAY Psalm 116:1-2

God hears you when you pray and ask Him for the things you need. He always is listening to you and you can talk to Him whenever and wherever you need to.

God can answer your prayers with a No, or a Wait, or a Yes. Color the praying hands to remind you to pray. Color the No red, the Wait yellow, and the Yes green to help you remember how God can answer prayer.

Pray Thank God for hearing your prayers.

WEDNESDAY Psalm 117:1-2

There are many things to praise God for. You need to praise God for His great love toward you and for His faithfulness.

How many hearts can you find in the design? Remember GREAT is God's love for you, so great He sent His Son, Jesus, to take the punishment for your sin.

Pray

Praise God for loving you.

THURSDAY Psalm 118:7

God has given you many different people in your life to help you in all sorts of ways.

Mom and Dad want to help their child learn to ride his bike. Complete the maze.

Pray

Tell God thank you for the people in your life who help you.

FRIDAY Psalm 118:28-29

The psalmist is not afraid to boldly praise the One True God. He wants to give God thanks and praise for he knows how good, loving, and wonderful God is.

Answer the questions to complete the crossword puzzle.

Across

2. The psalmist said God is?
4. What did the psalmist do?

Down

1. Who did the psalmist praise?
3. How many gods are there?

Word Bank

one
good
God
praise

Pray

Ask Jesus to make you bold and brave to make good choices.

SATURDAY Psalm 119:4

God has given you the Bible. In this most important book, you will find stories from history, the greatest teachings, and commands from God—things you ought to know and obey.

What is the most important book, the book that contains all truth? Look at the two pictures of the family reading the Bible. Can you find 7 differences?

Pray

Praise God for the Bible.

COMMENT CORNER

Parent or Leader, circle a comment and/or write your own.

You're special · You can do it · God loves you! · Nice job! · We're proud of you! · Keep it up · WOW!

DAYS COMPLETED

WEEK 4

"The B-I-B-L-E"

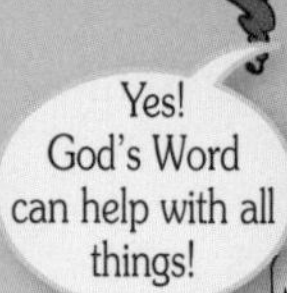

Can reading God's Word help me to know right from wrong?

Can reading God's Word help me to not be afraid?

Yes! God's Word can help with all things!

Yes!

What should you do with God's Word?

SUNDAY Psalm 119:11

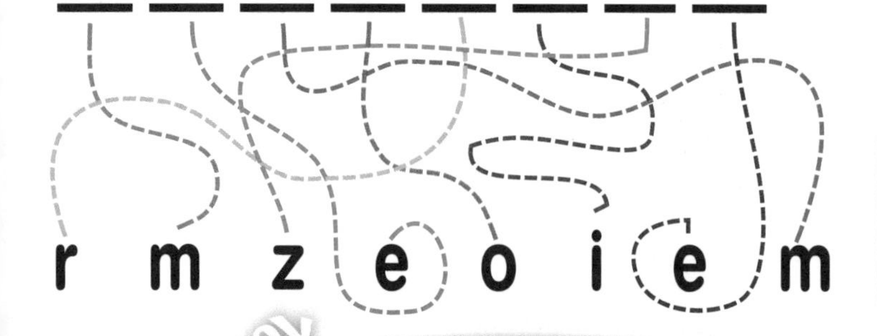

If you memorize God's Word, it will help you not to sin when you are tempted. Are you memorizing Bible verses? You should be. Like this psalmist, you need to hide God's Word in your heart (memorize it). That way you will know what His Word says and obey it, and not sin against God.

Pray Ask God to help you memorize His Word, the Bible.

MONDAY Psalm 119:24

Reading, studying, and knowing God's Word should be something you enjoy doing, a happy time. God's Word should guide all of your thoughts, words, and actions. It should be what tells you how to live. Ask God to help you understand and enjoy His Word and see it as wonderful.

Circle all the things you can read. Put a star next to the item that is all truth and the most important book you can read.

Pray Ask God to help you understand and enjoy His Word.

TUESDAY Psalm 119:28

Find these hidden words in the puzzle. Sad, Sin, God, Bible.

Draw a line through the things you should not say.

N	P	G	O	D
M	P	C	Y	N
P	E	S	A	D
Z	P	S	O	A
E	H	P	N	N
B	I	B	L	E
S	I	N	T	F
T	Q	X	Y	J

Pray Ask God to give you a heart that is sad when you sin.

WEDNESDAY Psalm 119:34

Ask God to help you understand His Word. Pray that He will help you remember it so that you will think about it during the day as you go to school, eat, and play.

Write down what you typically do each day at these times.

______

______

______

______

Pray Ask God to help you understand and remember His Word.

THURSDAY Psalm 119:44

You should want to obey God forever and ever, to do what is right and pleasing to God no matter what.

To complete this activity, you must obey the directions carefully. Look at the pictures. Say what they are. Write the letter sound you hear at the **end** of the word except for the last picture. Write the **first** sound you hear for the last picture.

This should be your desire.

___ ___ ___ ___ God.

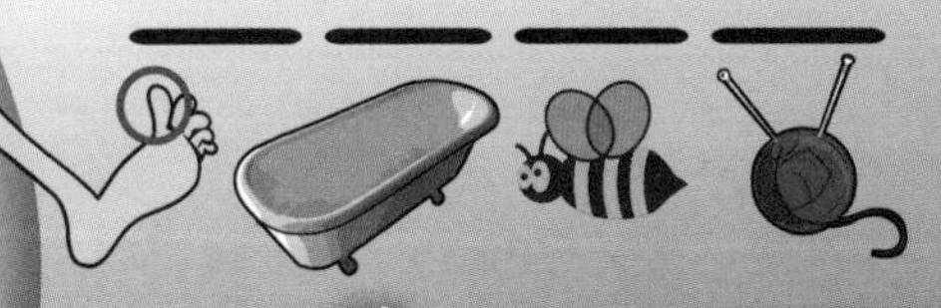

Pray Ask God to help you obey.

FRIDAY Psalm 119:50

God's Word is good for everything! God's Word can comfort you when you are afraid, worried, or upset.

Follow the path to the Bible. Write the letters on the line as you come to them. Then read the sentence.

God's Word will

___ ___ ___ ___ ___ ___ ___ you!

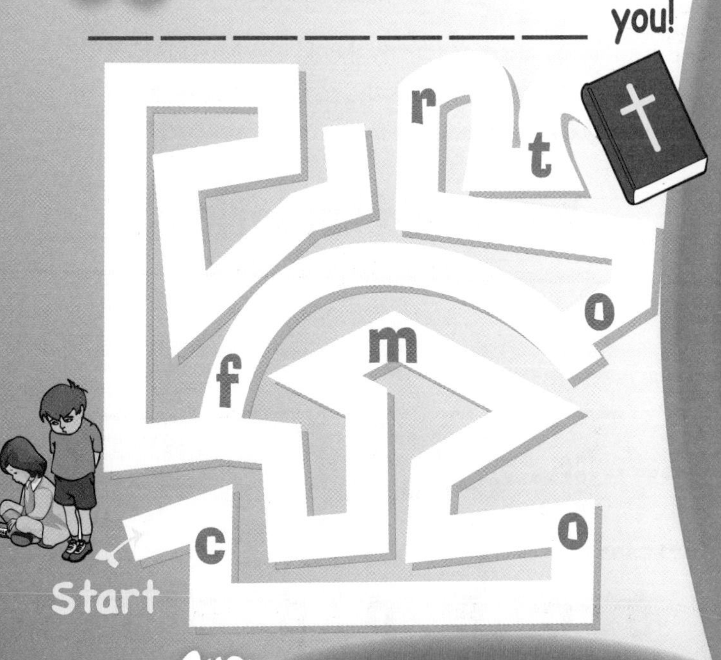

Pray Ask God to help you remember to read His Word.

SATURDAY Psalm 119:71

You can be thankful because troubled times are good. God can use them to teach you more about Him.

Use the first letter of every picture to complete the sentence.

God uses difficult times to help you

___ ___ ___ ___ ___

more about Him.

Pray Thank God that you can trust Him when you have problems.

COMMENT CORNER

Parent or Leader, circle a comment and/or write your own.

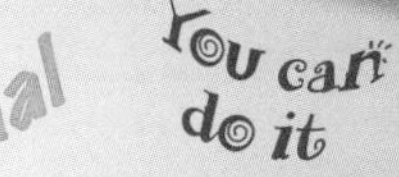

God loves you! Nice job! We're proud of you! Keep it up WOW!

DAYS COMPLETED

WEEK 5

"It's All About God"

SUNDAY Psalm 119:88

God will supply all your needs. He will even strengthen you to keep His commandments.

Draw a line to the things God supplies to strengthen your body, your mind, and your soul.

Fruit

Books

Candy

Bible

Vegetables

Video games

Church

Pray Thank God for helping you obey.

MONDAY Psalm 119:98-99

Do you want to be wise? Wisdom comes from knowing God's Word.

Complete the math problems.

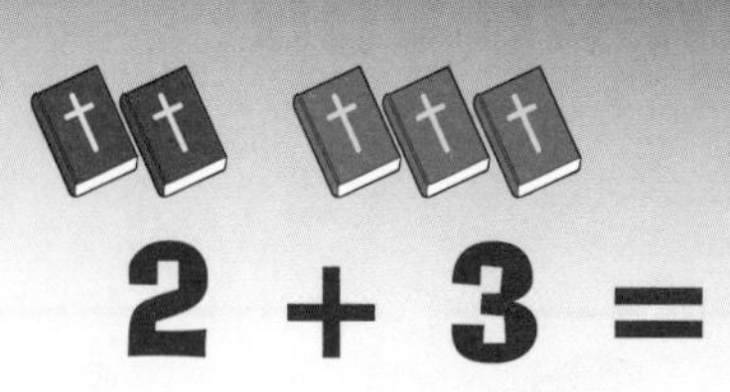

2 + 3 = ___

8 + 6 = ___

3 + 4 = ___

Pray Thank God for the wisdom in His Word.

TUESDAY Psalm 119:115

God wants you to be careful about whom you choose as your friends. Stay away from others who are mean or who enjoy breaking the rules. Friends like that will keep you from obeying God.

What kinds of friends should you have? Read what kind of friends the psalmist wanted in Psalm 119:63.

You should have friends who keep God's

_ _ _ _ _ _ _ _.

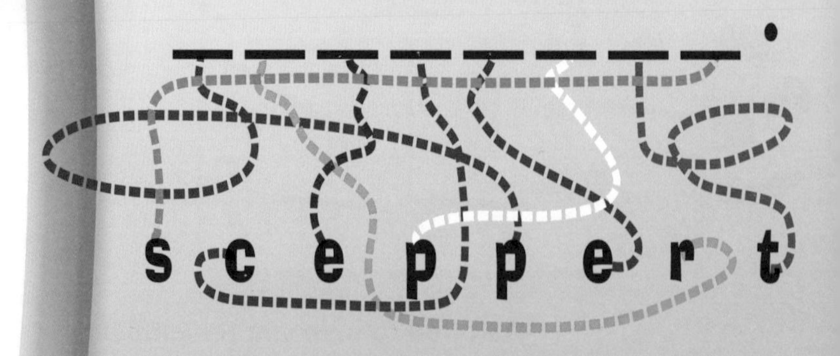

Pray Ask God to help you make good friends.

WEDNESDAY Psalm 119:128

You should love that which God says is good and hate that which God says is evil.

Circle the things you should love and cross out the things you should hate:

truthfulness

Kindness

forgiveness

stealing

saying bad words

lying

Pray Ask God to help you love good and hate bad.

THURSDAY Psalm 119:140

The psalmist loves God's Word.

Find the words: LOVE, GOD, and BIBLE in the puzzle below.

R	L	O	V	E	N
Q	M	U	Q	X	R
H	R	P	T	X	R
G	O	D	E	J	K
V	B	I	B	L	E
Z	T	P	T	D	I

Pray Thank God for His Word.

FRIDAY Psalm 119:158

The psalmist is upset because the people around him have forgotten and broken God's commands. You should hate all sin, your sin and others' sin. Sin is anything you think, do, or say that breaks one of God's commands.

Write the vowels to find the word's opposite.

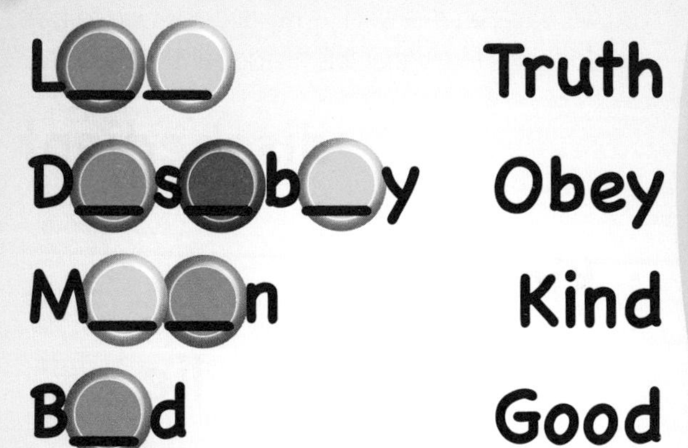

Pray Ask God to help you hate sin.

SATURDAY Psalm 119:176

You are like a lost sheep that has wandered away. You have chosen to sin against God. You deserve to be punished for your disobedience. But there is good news: God wants to bring home all His lost sheep. He wants you to repent of your sin and believe that Jesus died on the cross, taking the punishment for your sin.

Color this picture of a shepherd bringing home his lost sheep. Jesus is your shepherd, the only way home to Heaven.

Pray Thank Jesus for being a wonderful, caring Shepherd.

COMMENT CORNER Parent or Leader, circle a comment and/or write your own.

You're special · You can do it · God loves you! · Nice job! · We're proud of you! · Keep it up · WOW!

DAYS COMPLETED

WEEK 6

"Letters to Grow By"

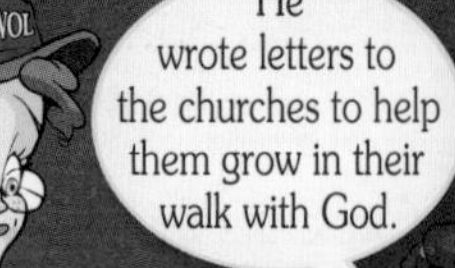

Philippians is the letter Paul wrote to the church in Philippi.

He wrote letters to the churches to help them grow in their walk with God.

Paul was a great missionary who started many churches.

SUNDAY Philippians 1:6

Have you let God begin to work in your heart by asking Him to be your Savior from sin? Color the heart that answers that question. If not, you can ask Him to be your Savior today. Ask your parent or an adult at church for help.

YES

NO

When God begins a work in your heart, He will continue it until you see Him face-to-face.

Pray

Tell Jesus thank you for never giving up on you.

MONDAY Philippians 1:9-11

Paul prayed that the way the people lived would make Jesus happy. He prayed they would produce the "fruit of right living."

Use the color key to color the fruit.

1+2 = yellow
2+3 = red
3+4 = purple
4+5 = orange

Pray

Ask Jesus to help you do things today that will make Him happy.

TUESDAY Philippians 1:20-21

Paul wanted to live to please Jesus. Paul wanted to please Jesus in everything He did.

Draw a line to match the opposites. Circle one thing you will work on this week. Pray and ask God to help you do things today that will please Him.

disobedient

kind

lie

obedient

mean

truth

Pray

Ask Jesus to help you want to please Him today.

WEDNESDAY Philippians 1:27

Paul tells the believers to work together. God wants Christians to get along with each other.

Do you have trouble getting along with someone? Write that person's name on the line. Pray and ask God to help you get along with that person.

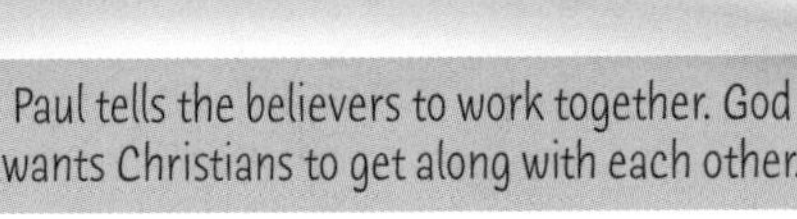

Pray Ask God to help you get along with others today.

THURSDAY Philippians 2:6-7

Jesus, Who is God, came to earth in the body of a man. He showed you how to be a servant.

Write the letters that are in the triangles on the lines to complete the sentence.

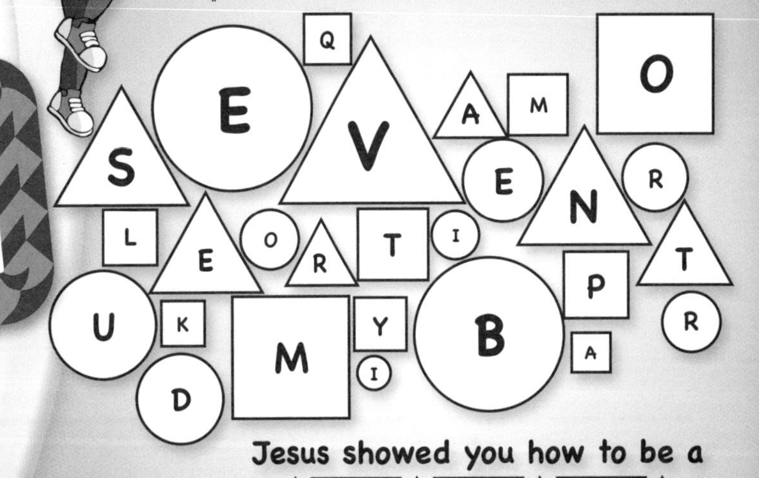

Jesus showed you how to be a

Pray Ask God to help you be a servant like Jesus.

FRIDAY Philippians 2:14-15

When you do everything without complaining and arguing, others will know you belong to God. You will shine like the stars in the sky.

Complete the dot-to-dot. Count by 10's. When you are finished, pray and ask God to help you do things without complaining and arguing.

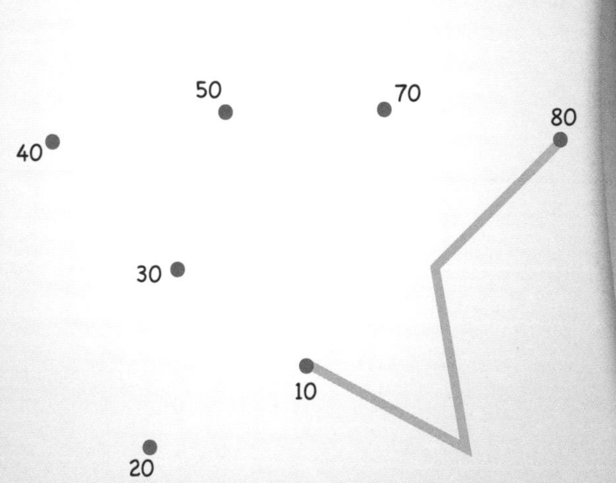

Pray Ask Jesus to help you do things without complaining.

SATURDAY Philippians 2:19

Timothy was Paul's young helper. Timothy was a faithful servant. Paul trusted Timothy to do a good job.

It is important that you do your best when given a job. Start at the arrow and write every other letter on the lines.

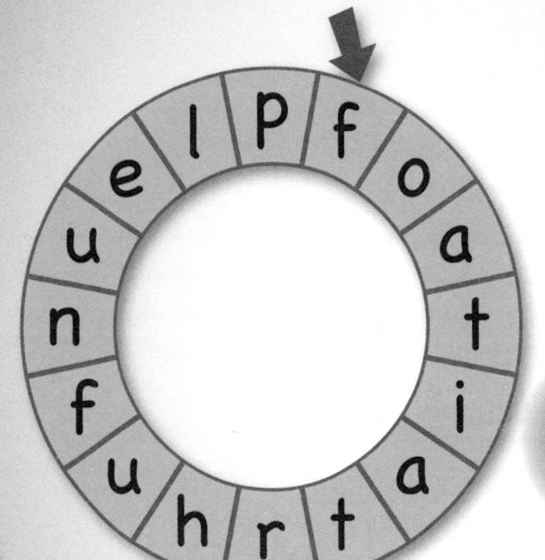

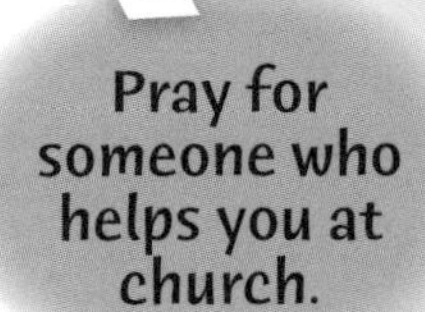

Pray for someone who helps you at church.

COMMENT CORNER

Parent or Leader, circle a comment and/or write your own.

DAYS COMPLETED

You're special · You can do it · God loves you! · Nice job! · We're proud of you! · Keep it up · WOW!

WEEK 7

Paul told the church not to worry about anything, but to pray instead.

Paul kept his eyes on God and didn't give up.

SUNDAY Philippians 2:29-30

Fill in the blanks with the first letter of each picture to find out who you should look up to.

__ __ __ __ __ __ __ __ __ __

Pray

Pray for a missionary family today.

MONDAY Philippians 3:1

Paul told the people to be joyful. You should be joyful if you belong to God.

Complete the sentence.

Paul told the people to be:

____ smart

____ rich

____ grumpy

____ joyful

TUESDAY Philippians 3:13-14

Trace the letters to see what you should do when it is hard to do right.

God loves you. He wants to share His loving-kindness with you. He wants to rescue you from the penalty of sin. To learn more, talk to your parent or an adult at church. Write your name on the line and color the hearts.

On

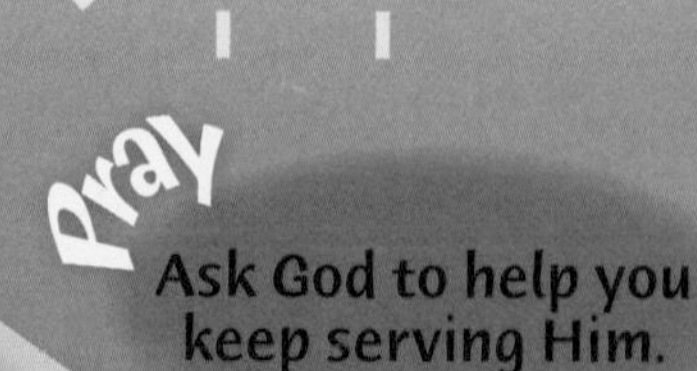

WEDNESDAY Philippians 3:18-19

Paul said so many people have their eyes on the things of this world. You should keep your eyes on God and His kingdom.

Circle the things you think Paul meant by "earthly things." Remember to keep your focus on God.

Church
Toys
Prayer
Friendship
TV
Money
Sharing the Gospel
Bible

Pray Ask God to help you keep your eyes on Him.

THURSDAY Philippians 4:6-7

You should not worry about anything, but pray instead. When you do this God will give you peace.

Write something you worry about inside the hands. Pray about it each day for a week.

Pray Pray for something you are worried about.

FRIDAY Philippians 4:8

You should only think about things that are true and pure.

Write in the letters u and e to find what you should think about.

Pray Ask God to help you to have true and pure thoughts.

SATURDAY Philippians 4:18-19

Because of their gifts, Paul had all he needed. God will meet your needs, too.

Color the spaces with a diamond to read the message.

Pray Thank God that He meets all your needs.

COMMENT CORNER

Parent or Leader, circle a comment and/or write your own.

You're special · You can do it · God loves you! · Nice job! · We're proud of you! · Keep it up · WOW!

DAYS COMPLETED

WEEK 8
"God's Helpers"
Can I be a helper?
Even kids can help God?
This week we will learn about some of God's helpers.
Yes! Miriam was Moses' sister and a helper!
SUNDAY
Exodus 1:12-14
Find and circle the 5 hidden happy faces to remind you that God can use you to help someone else be happier.
The Israelites were Pharaoh's slaves. God knew they were suffering so He sent Moses to be their helper.
Pray
Ask God to show you someone who is sad that you can help be happy.
TUESDAY Exodus 2:4
Miriam helped her mother watch over her brother Moses.
MONDAY Exodus 1:17
Find the three underlined words and circle each one.
The Hebrew women did right and kept the Israelite babies safe even though Pharaoh wanted them dead.
Color the heart that does right and pleases God.
M O T H E R
V Q C W M F
M O S E S W
M I R I A M
L D B A X I
kindness love
hate selfish
Pray
Ask God to help you do 2 things to help your mother today.
Pray
Ask God to help you do right even when it's hard.

WEDNESDAY Exodus 2:16-17

Moses was kind to the shepherd girls by drawing the water for them out of the well.

What should you be all the time? Unscramble the letters on the sheep to see.

Pray Ask God to help you be kind.

____ ____ ____ ____

THURSDAY Exodus 3:3-4

God called Moses and asked him to be His helper for the Israelites. Moses not only heard, but he obeyed.

Help Moses obey by finding the path to the burning bush.

Pray Ask God to help you obey Him.

FRIDAY Exodus 3:13-14

Moses had a big job to do and God was going to help him. God is always ready to be your helper when you need Him. He is there any time of the day.

Write the time on the lines.

___:___

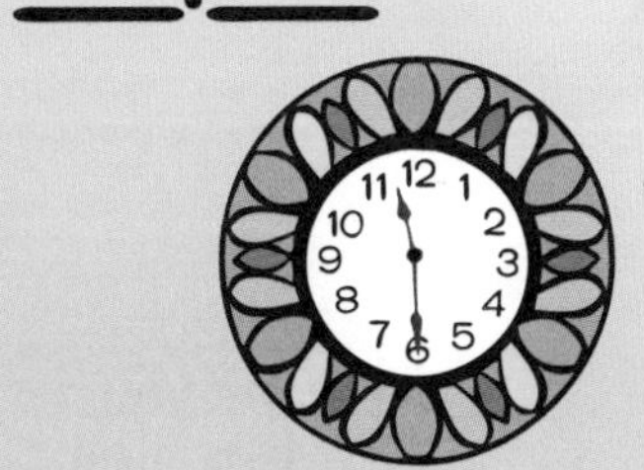

___:___

___:___

Pray Thank God that He will help you.

SATURDAY Exodus 4:11-12

God told Moses He would help him speak to Pharaoh the king. God made your mouth. He will help you to speak kind words to others.

Fill the mouth with kind words by drawing lines from the kind words to the mouth.

May I pray for you?

Can I help you?

I love you.

Go away.

Shut up.

Come to church with me.

Pray Ask God to use your mouth to say kind words.

COMMENT CORNER

Parent or Leader, circle a comment and/or write your own.

You're special · You can do it · God loves you! · Nice job! · We're proud of you! · Keep it up · WOW!

DAYS COMPLETED

WEEK 9

"Moses Supposes God's Way Is Best"

SUNDAY Exodus 4:27-28

When can you be a helper?
Unscramble the letters to answer the question.

3=Y 4=T 1=A 6=M 7=E 2=N 5=I

Aaron loved his brother and went to meet him in the wilderness. Moses needed help to do God's work, so Aaron went to join Moses.

Pray Ask God to help you be a helper today.

MONDAY Exodus 5:2

Pharaoh did not want to obey God's voice. When you read the Bible, you can hear what God says.

Put a star by the best answer to finish the sentence.

As a Christian you should...

not listen to God's Word.

listen to God's Word.

listen to and obey God's Word.

Pray Ask God to help you always hear and obey the Bible.

TUESDAY Exodus 5:22-23

Moses was having problems. Pharaoh was not listening to him and the Israelites were suffering. Moses called on God to help him.

Unscramble the letters in the praying hands to see Who to ask for help in times of trouble.

___ ___ ___

Pray Tell God thank you for listening when you pray.

WEDNESDAY Exodus 6:7

God loved the Israelites and wanted to free them from Pharaoh. He wanted to be their God. God wants you to be His child, too.

If you are His child, draw a picture of yourself on the right side of the page. If you aren't God's child, draw a picture of yourself on the left side of the page and talk to your parents or an adult at church about how you can become God's child.

Pray Tell God you love Him.

THURSDAY Exodus 7:6

Moses and Aaron did all God told them to do. They obeyed God.

Find the hidden letters O, B, E, Y in the picture and write them on the line.

____

Pray Ask God to help you obey all the time.

FRIDAY Exodus 7:14

Pharaoh's heart was hard. That means he didn't want to believe in God. God is sad when people have hard hearts and don't believe in Him.

Hold your book up to a mirror to reveal what kind of heart God wants. Write it in the box.

TRAƎH TFOS A

Pray Ask God to help you obey Him.

SATURDAY Exodus 8:6

Moses told Pharaoh to let God's people go. Pharaoh wouldn't listen, so God let terrible things happen to Pharaoh.

One of the terrible things was that some animals came out of the river and covered Egypt. What were they? To find out, color the spaces that have a Y yellow. Color the other spaces green.

Pray Tell God thank you for taking care of you.

COMMENT CORNER

Parent or Leader, circle a comment and/or write your own.

You're special · You can do it · God loves you! · Nice job! · We're proud of you! · Keep it up · WOW!

DAYS COMPLETED

WEEK 10

"Mighty is Our God"

SUNDAY Exodus 8:24

Pharaoh would not listen to God, so God sent swarms of flies to cover Egypt.

What do you need to do so you won't be like Pharaoh? Color all the bugs that contain lowercase letters, and then copy the CAPITAL letters onto the lines.

I T N L S E O T O D G e d b

_______ __ ___

Pray Thank God for your ears that help you listen to Him.

MONDAY Exodus 9:1

God wanted His people to worship Him. Pharaoh didn't want the people worshipping God. You can worship God wherever you are.

Check the places where you can worship God.

- ☐ The park
- ☐ At school
- ☐ At church
- ☐ At home

Pray Tell God that He is great.

TUESDAY Exodus 9:14-16

God showed His power to Pharaoh so that all would know that He is God. God wants everyone to know Him.

Write the first letter of each picture to see Who is mighty.

___ ___ ___

Pray Thank God that He is more powerful than anyone.

WEDNESDAY Exodus 9:27

Pharaoh admitted that he had sinned and that God is right.

Do you try not to sin? Put a happy face by the things a Christian should do and a sad face by the things that are sin. Tell God when you sin so He can forgive you.

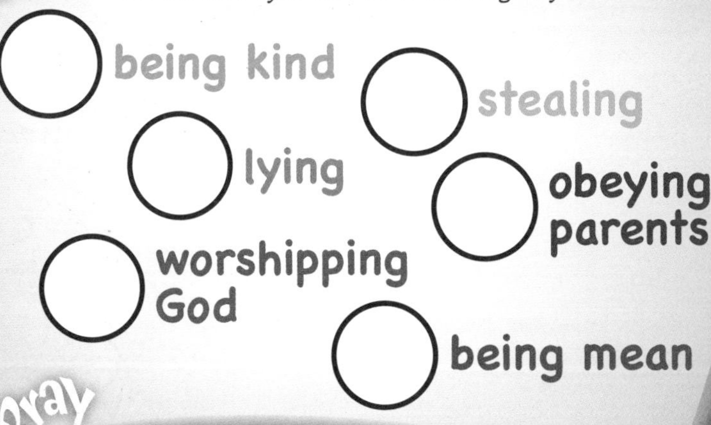

Pray Tell God thank you for hearing you when you pray.

THURSDAY Exodus 10:3

Pharaoh was proud and would not humble himself before God. A humble heart is what God wants you to have.

Find the 3 underlined words that Candice spoke. Look for them in the puzzle and circle each one. Do you have a humble heart?

G	F	O	B	M	D
H	E	A	R	T	O
B	Q	H	G	O	D
H	U	M	B	L	E

Pray Ask God to help you have a humble heart.

FRIDAY Exodus 10:23

God sent many plagues on Egypt. One was a plague of darkness where all Egypt was dark, but the children of God had the sun where they lived. If you are God's child, you have the light of God in you.

Count by 2's to complete the dot-to-dot. This will remind you to be a light for God. On the line write the name of a person you can tell about Jesus.

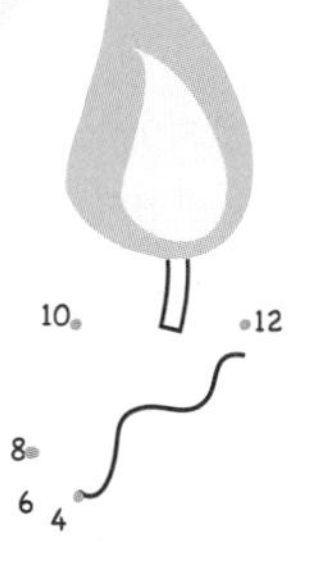

2 14

Pray Ask God to help you shine for Him.

____

SATURDAY Exodus 11:7

God protected His children the Israelites.

If you are God's child He will protect you, too. Use the first letter of each picture to complete this sentence.

YOU DO NOT NEED TO BE

___ ___ ___ ___ ___ ___

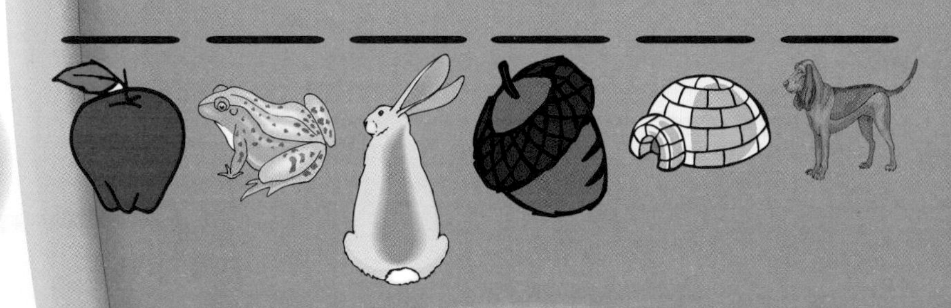

Pray Tell God thank you for His protection.

COMMENT CORNER Parent or Leader, circle a comment and/or write your own.

You're special · You can do it · God loves you! · Nice job! · We're proud of you! · Keep it up · WOW!

DAYS COMPLETED

WEEK 11
"God is Our Champion"
I am so glad that God is my champion!
He's always there when we need Him!
No one is more powerful than God!
SUNDAY Exodus 12:3, 5
Color the picture and thank Jesus for dying for your sin.
Before Jesus came, a lamb was chosen to be sacrificed. It had to be perfect without any marks on it. Jesus was the ultimate sacrifice for everyone's sin when He died on the cross.
Pray
Thank Jesus for being the Lamb of God.
MONDAY Exodus 12:17
God wanted the Israelites to remember how He protected them from the armies of Egypt. God's on your side! Call on Him when you are in trouble and He will protect you.
God will
_ _ _ _ _ _ _ you.
p e t t o r c
Pray
Thank God for always being there to help you.
TUESDAY Exodus 12:29-31
Passover was a symbol that someday Jesus, who is the Lamb of God, would come to the earth to save you from your sin.
Jesus came and died for you so your sin could be forgiven. Write your name on the cross if you have asked Jesus to forgive your sin. If you haven't, talk to your parents or an adult at church.
Pray
Thank Jesus for His great love for you.

WEDNESDAY Exodus 12:42

God wanted Passover to always be remembered so no one would forget what God did.

Never forget that Jesus is the Lamb of God! Find the 3 hidden lambs in the picture and circle them.

Pray

Thank Jesus for being the Lamb of God.

THURSDAY Exodus 13:10

The Israelites were to always remember how God brought them out of Egypt with His mighty hand. You should always remember what God has done for you.

Write a list of all God has done for you.

Pray

Tell God thank you for one thing He has done for you.

FRIDAY Exodus 13:21-22

God led the Israelites with a pillar of cloud by day and a pillar of fire by night. He leads you with His Word, the Bible.

What should you read every day? Work the addition problems. Use the answers to fill in the missing word.

___+___=___ ___+___+___=___

___+___=___ ___+___=___

2 = B 4 = E 3 = I 5 = L

What should you read every day?

_ _ _ _ _
2 3 2 5 4

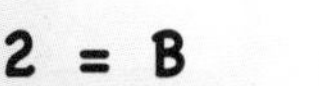

Pray

Ask God to help you read the Bible every day.

SATURDAY Exodus 14:13

Moses told the Israelites not to be afraid because God would save them. You don't have to be afraid. You can ask God for help.

Draw a picture of something that makes you afraid. Ask God for His help with this fear.

Pray

Ask God to help you when you are afraid.

COMMENT CORNER

Parent or Leader, circle a comment and/or write your own.

DAYS COMPLETED

You're special · You can do it · God loves you! · Nice job! · We're proud of you! · Keep it up · WOW!

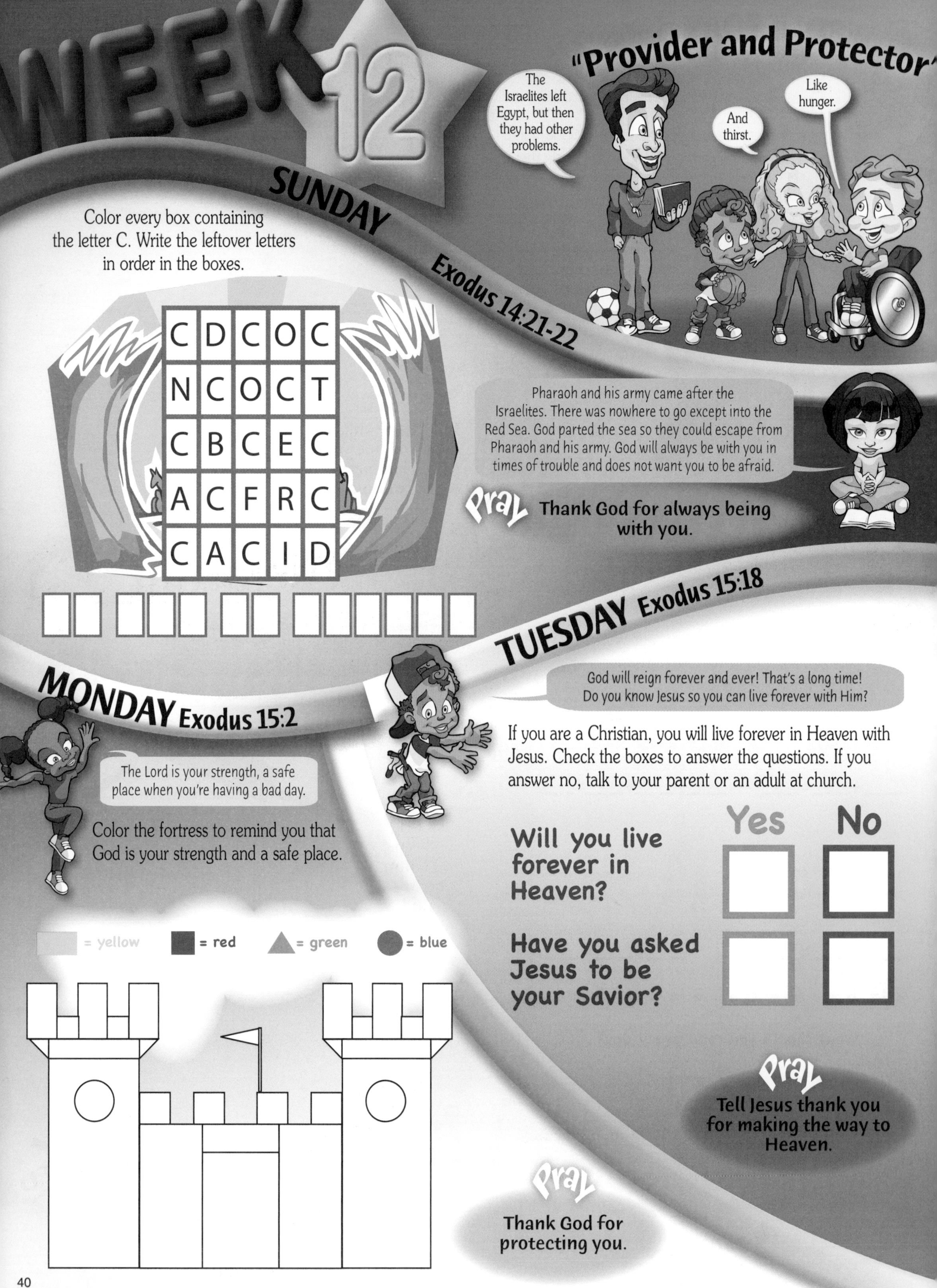
WEEK 12
"Provider and Protector"
The Israelites left Egypt, but then they had other problems.
And thirst.
Like hunger.
SUNDAY
Exodus 14:21-22
Color every box containing the letter C. Write the leftover letters in order in the boxes.
C D C O C
N C O C T
C B C E C
A C F R C
C A C I D
Pharaoh and his army came after the Israelites. There was nowhere to go except into the Red Sea. God parted the sea so they could escape from Pharaoh and his army. God will always be with you in times of trouble and does not want you to be afraid.
Pray
Thank God for always being with you.
MONDAY Exodus 15:2
The Lord is your strength, a safe place when you're having a bad day.
Color the fortress to remind you that God is your strength and a safe place.
= yellow
= red
= green
= blue
Pray
Thank God for protecting you.
TUESDAY Exodus 15:18
God will reign forever and ever! That's a long time! Do you know Jesus so you can live forever with Him?
If you are a Christian, you will live forever in Heaven with Jesus. Check the boxes to answer the questions. If you answer no, talk to your parent or an adult at church.
Yes
No
Will you live forever in Heaven?
Have you asked Jesus to be your Savior?
Pray
Tell Jesus thank you for making the way to Heaven.
40

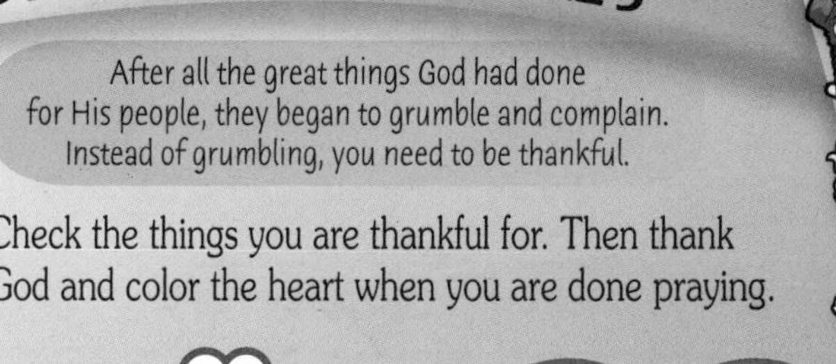

WEDNESDAY Exodus 16:2-3

After all the great things God had done for His people, they began to grumble and complain. Instead of grumbling, you need to be thankful.

Check the things you are thankful for. Then thank God and color the heart when you are done praying.

- clothes
- family
- friends
- food
- toys
- house
- church
- Jesus

Pray Ask God to give you a thankful heart.

THURSDAY Exodus 16:15

The Israelites had no food to eat so God provided manna for them.

Find 5 hidden foods in the picture and circle them. Be sure to thank God for your food each time you have a meal.

Pray Thank God for your favorite foods.

FRIDAY Exodus 16:31

Manna tasted like honey. God's Word is like honey and it feeds your heart.

God lets you know what He wants you to do through the Bible. Start at the arrow and write every other letter on the lines.

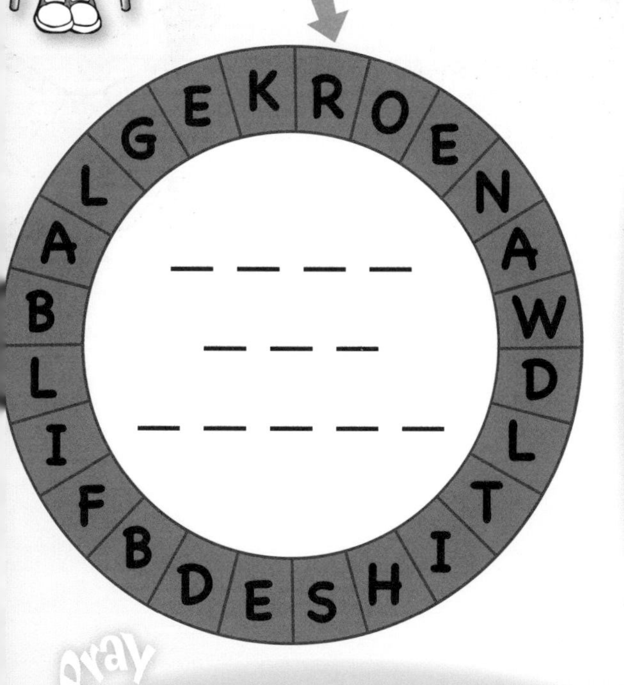

Pray Thank God for His Word, the Bible.

SATURDAY Exodus 17:5-6

The Israelites had no water to drink. God had Moses strike a rock and water came pouring out. God took care of His people.

Copy the letters along the trail into the puzzle boxes.

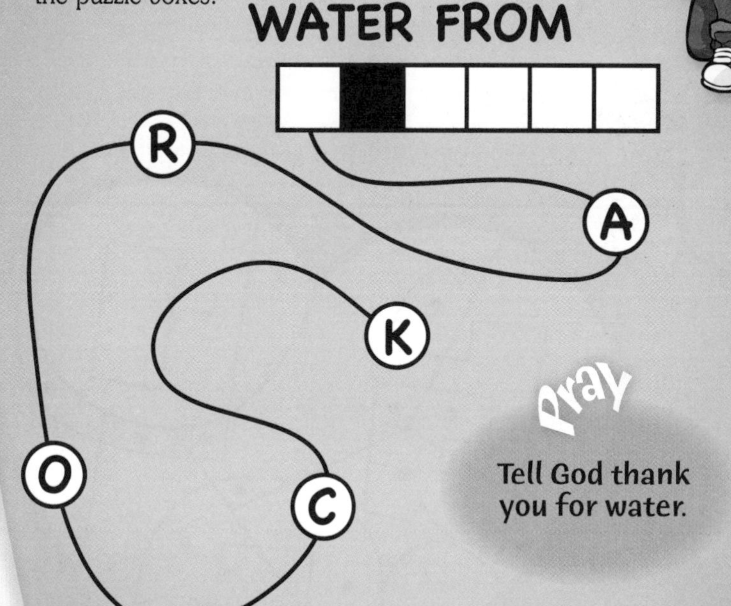

Pray Tell God thank you for water.

COMMENT CORNER

Parent or Leader, circle a comment and/or write your own.

You're special · You can do it · God loves you! · Nice job! · We're proud of you! · Keep it up · WOW!

DAYS COMPLETED

WEEK 13
"God's Rules Rock"
Does anyone know what God's rules are called?
The Ten Commandments
Yes, not the ten suggestions.
SUNDAY
Exodus 19:8
Find the letters in the picture that spell what you should do with God's commands. Write the letters on the tablets.
O
Y
E
B
God's people promised they would obey all God said. That's a promise you should try to keep also, but you can only do it with Jesus' help. It's too hard to do by yourself.
Pray
Ask God to help you obey His rules.
MONDAY Exodus 19:16-17
When the Israelites heard how powerfully God spoke from Mt. Sinai, they knew they could trust Him.
Color the spaces with dots in them to find out Whom you can trust.
Pray
Ask God to help you trust Him more.
TUESDAY Exodus 20:12
God wants you to honor your father and mother. This means obeying and respecting them.
Draw a picture of your dad or mom to remind you to obey them.
Pray
Ask God to help you to obey your parents.

WEDNESDAY Exodus 24:7

When the Israelites heard God's rules; they said they would obey them.

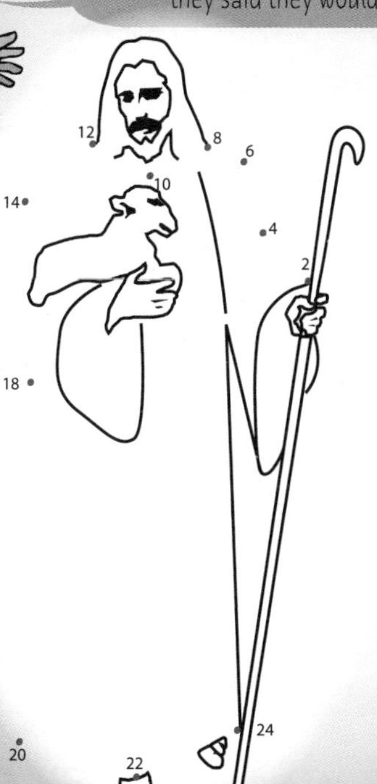

Count by 2s to complete the dot-to-dot of Jesus, and then color it. Remember to obey Jesus' rules!

Pray

Ask Jesus to help you to listen and obey.

THURSDAY Exodus 25:1-2

God wanted an offering from the Israelites. They gave many of their belongings to do the work of God.

Draw a line from the pictures of things you can give as an offering to the word God.

God

Time

Pray

Ask God to help you give something today for Him.

FRIDAY Exodus 25:22

God spoke to Moses like you would speak to a friend. God considered Moses His friend.

Are you a friend of God? Put a happy face by the things a friend of God would do and a sad face by the things a friend of God shouldn't do.

love

share

lie

be mean

praise God

Pray

Thank God for being your friend.

SATURDAY Exodus 31:15

The Sabbath is our Sunday. God wants you to keep Sunday holy. One way to do that is by going to church.

You can go to church on Sunday to hear the Bible being taught. Color the picture.

△ = red

○ = yellow

□ = blue

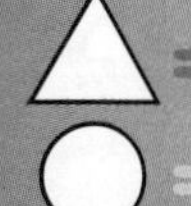

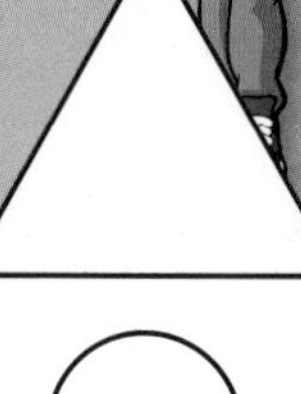

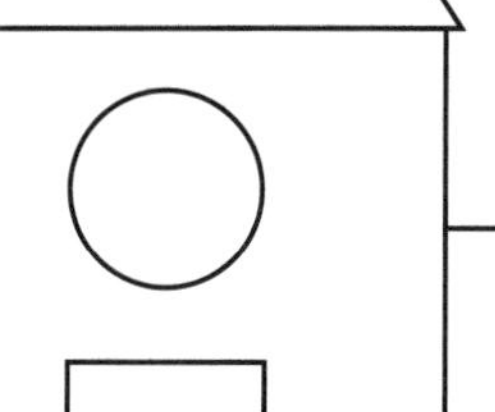

Pray

Tell God thank you for your church.

COMMENT CORNER

Parent or Leader, circle a comment and/or write your own.

DAYS COMPLETED

You're special · You can do it · God loves you! · Nice job! · We're proud of you! · Keep it up · WOW!

WEEK 14

"Friends Forever"

SUNDAY Exodus 32:8

Put an X through things that can become idols in your life.

toys

TV

friends

The Israelites were worshipping a golden calf. You are not to worship idols. Anything you put before God is an idol.

Pray Ask God to help you get rid of any idols.

MONDAY Exodus 33:17

God knew Moses' name. He knows your name, too.

You are so important to God that He knows your name. Write your name on the palm of God's hand.

____

Pray Thank God that He knows you and loves you.

TUESDAY Exodus 34:10

God made a covenant with the Israelites. A covenant is a promise. God is always faithful and does what He says.

Rainbows are signs of God's promises. Color the rainbow using the color code.

red
orange
yellow
green
violet

Pray Thank God for keeping His promises.

WEDNESDAY Exodus 34:29-30

After Moses had spent time with God, His face shone so brightly he had to wear a covering. When you know Jesus and obey Him, people will see a difference in you.

Connect the opposite words to see what a difference God can make in your life.

sad	love
lying	truth
being mean	happy
hate	kindness

Pray Ask God to help you shine for Him.

THURSDAY Exodus 40:15-16

Moses helped get the priests ready to serve God. All people of all ages can serve God. Even children!

God can use you to do special things. Choose one thing you can do today and circle it.

Share
Tell someone about Jesus
Sing praises
Help a friend

Pray Ask God to help you serve Him today.

FRIDAY Exodus 40:26-27

Moses burned special incense to God. Incense is a symbol of prayer. God likes your prayers. They rise up and smell like sweet incense to Him.

God loves to hear your prayers. They are like sweet smelling perfume to Him. Color the picture using the code.

Pray Tell God how much you love Him.

1 = purple 2 = brown 3 = red 4 = yellow

SATURDAY Exodus 40:29

The Israelites worshipped with burnt offerings and sacrifices. Jesus was the ultimate sacrifice and offering when He died for your sin.

Draw a line from 5 to 60 counting by 5s to see what Jesus died on. After you're done, tell Jesus thank you for dying for your sin.

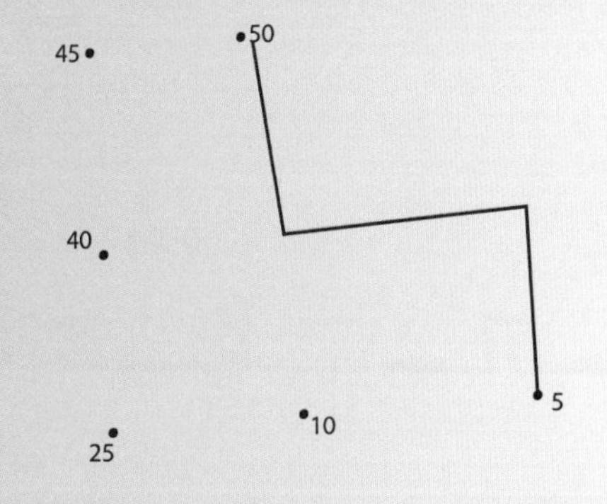

Pray Tell Jesus thank you for dying for your sin.

20 • 15

COMMENT CORNER

Parent or Leader, circle a comment and/or write your own.

You're special · You can do it · God loves you! · Nice job! · We're proud of you! · Keep it up · WOW!

DAYS COMPLETED

WEEK 15

SUNDAY 2 Timothy 1:6

When you ask Jesus to be your Savior, your faith is like a small flame. Paul says to fan it into a big flame.

Air fans a real flame. Unscramble the words to see what can "fan" your faith. Circle the one you will do today.

nsi apie _ _ _ g _ r _ _ s _ Music

mimroe ssev _ e _ _ _ _ _ z _ Bible _ _ r _ e _

Pray Ask Jesus to help you fan your faith into a big flame.

MONDAY 2 Timothy 1:8-10

You don't have to be afraid of dying because Jesus destroyed death.

How did Jesus destroy death? Do the math.

7 +2	5 +2		5 +4
C _	m _		B _ c K

3 +2	2 +2	3 +4
T _	L _	f _ .

Code: 7=E, 4=I, 9=A, 5=O

Pray Thank God that Jesus has the power to destroy death.

TUESDAY 2 Timothy 1:16-17

Paul said that Onesiphorus encouraged him. How can you encourage a servant of God?

Cross out the wrong answer. Circle the one you will do today.

pray for them

call them a bad name

write them a note

bake them cookies

Pray Ask God to help you encourage one friend today.

WEDNESDAY 2 Timothy 2:7

Paul told Timothy to think about God's Word and God would give him the ability to understand it.

Write the missing letter to find places where you can think about your memory verse. Ask God to help you understand what your verse means.

_ed

_us

_ike trail

_all game

_each

Pray

Ask God to help you understand your memory verse today.

THURSDAY 2 Timothy 2:13

God, by definition, has to be faithful.

Draw a line to connect the word to the definition.

Piglet	Burns
Hot	Keeps His Word
Snake	Reptile
God	Baby pig

Pray

Thank God that He never changes His mind.

FRIDAY 2 Timothy 2:18

God says to turn away from wickedness. Stop doing wrong.

Color the traffic signal red if you should stop an activity. Color it green if you should continue the activity. Color it yellow if you should limit how often you do it.

Pray

Ask God to be the boss in your choices today.

SATURDAY 2 Timothy 2:24

Paul tells Timothy to not quarrel and to be kind to everyone.

HARD

Write the names of three people it is easy to be kind to. Now write the names of three people it is hard to be kind to.

Pray

Ask God to help you today be kind to someone who is not kind to you.

COMMENT CORNER

Parent or Leader, circle a comment and/or write your own.

DAYS COMPLETED

You're special You can do it God loves you! Nice job! We're proud of you!

WOW!

WEEK 16

"Forgiving Friends"

Sarah really made me mad today when she didn't pass me the ball.

I think she just didn't see you.

The choice is up to you. Will you be a forgiving friend?

Jesus would want you to forgive her.

SUNDAY 2 Timothy 3:2

List 5 things you are grateful for today.

1. ____
2. ____
3. ____
4. ____
5. ____

Are you ever ungrateful? That is a sin.

Pray

Tell God one thing you are grateful for today.

MONDAY 2 Timothy 3:12

God always has a plan to use even bad things to help you be more like Him.

Fill in the vowels to see people that God made more like Him through bad things that happened.

N__ __H W__S __N __ FL__ __D.

D__N__ __L W__S F__D T__ TH__ L__ __NS.

P__ __L W__S M__D__ BL__ND.

Pray

Ask Jesus to help you remember Him even when bad things happen.

TUESDAY 2 Timothy 3:14

Paul taught Timothy about God. He told him to continue in what he had learned.

Write the number to show the correct order.

Pray

Ask God to help you make good choices.

WEDNESDAY 2 Timothy 4:1

A referee makes the rules for soccer. God makes the rules for Heaven.

Use the code to see God's rules for going to Heaven.

A k Je o for ive yo r in and co e in o yo r ear .

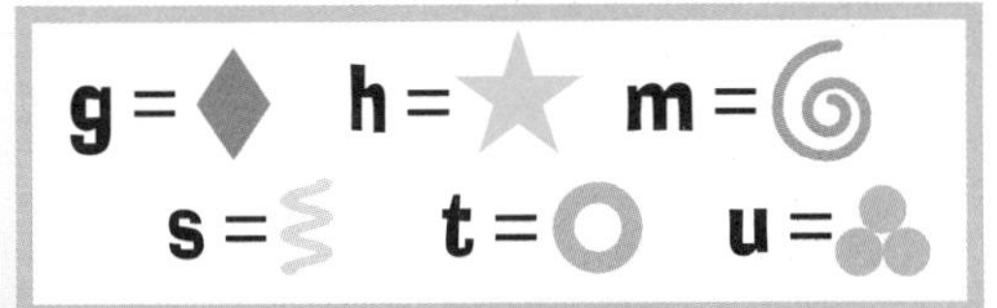

Pray

Thank God that you can know His rules to go to Heaven.

THURSDAY 2 Timothy 4:5

Paul told Timothy that he could control his choices.

Circle 3 ways you could correctly respond when your friend makes you mad.

count to 10

call her names

play with someone else

pray

Pray

Thank God for giving you the power to make good choices.

FRIDAY 2 Timothy 4:11

Friends can work together to help others.

Count the friends in each group. Add each number together to see how many friends helped.

______

______

______

Pray

Ask God to help you and your friends work together.

SATURDAY 2 Timothy 4:16

Paul forgave his friends when they let him down.

Put a check beside each statement that would hurt your feelings and decide to forgive the next time it happens.

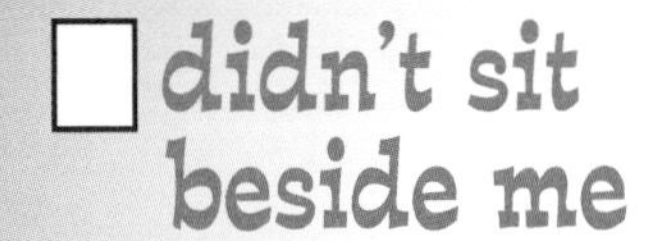

☐ didn't invite me to her party

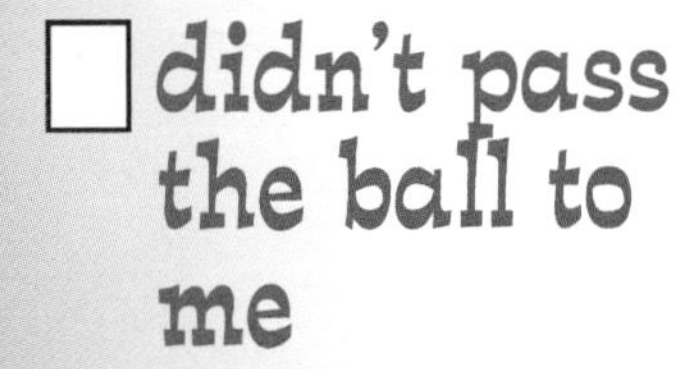

☐ didn't share their candy

Ask God to help you forgive your friends when they hurt your feelings.

COMMENT CORNER

Parent or Leader, circle a comment and/or write your own.

You're special · You can do it · God loves you! · Nice job! · We're proud of you! · Keep it up · WOW!

DAYS COMPLETED

"Rock with Respect"

SUNDAY Nahum 1:7

Where do you go when you are afraid?
Draw a line to the right answer.

Squirrel	Nest
Rabbit	Tree
Child	Hole
Bird	Pray to God

God is your refuge in times of trouble.

Pray

Ask God to help you remember to pray when you are afraid.

MONDAY Malachi 1:6

God says that you are to show respect, or honor, to your dad and to God.

Fill in the missing letters to see 3 ways to show honor.

O_e_

y b

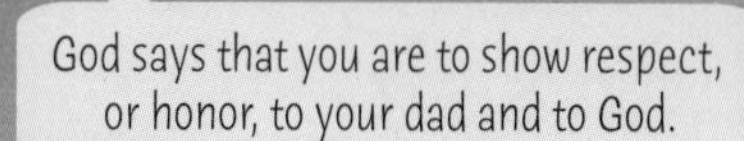

_i_te_

s n L

T_n_ _f v_ic_

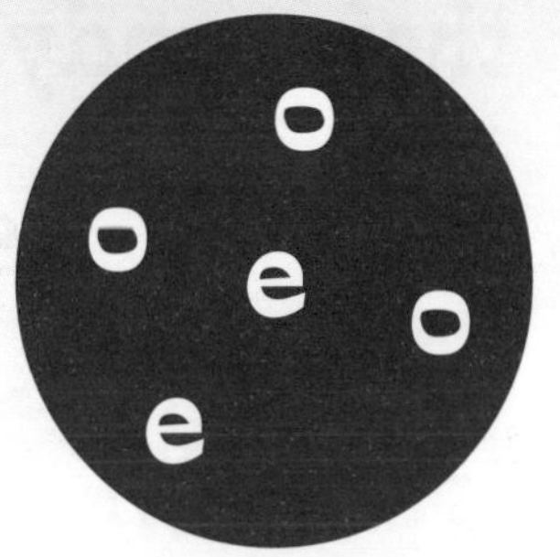

TUESDAY Malachi 2:2

God says you can choose, or set your heart, to honor Him.

Set the clock to 5:00.
Circle the number to set the remote to channel 2.
Circle the child set to honor God.

Pray

Tell God that you choose to obey Him.

Pray

Ask God to help you honor your dad today by obeying him the first time.

WEDNESDAY Malachi 2:17

God does not like it when you say it is OK to do something wrong.

Put a T for True and F for False.

A small lie is not sin.

He made me hit him.

Bad choices are sin.

God does not care if I whine.

It is OK to do wrong if no one sees me.

Pray
Ask God to help you see when you sin.

THURSDAY Malachi 3:6

God doesn't change and His rules don't change. There is only one way to have your sin forgiven.

Solve the riddle to find out how sins are forgiven.

It is the color of one of the stripes in the American flag.

It has twin vowels.

Jesus shed it for our sins.

It comes out when you are cut.

______

Pray
Thank God that He is the same yesterday, today, and tomorrow.

FRIDAY Malachi 3:14

God wants you to know that it is important to obey Him.

Disobedience is sin. Follow the lines to see one way to obey.

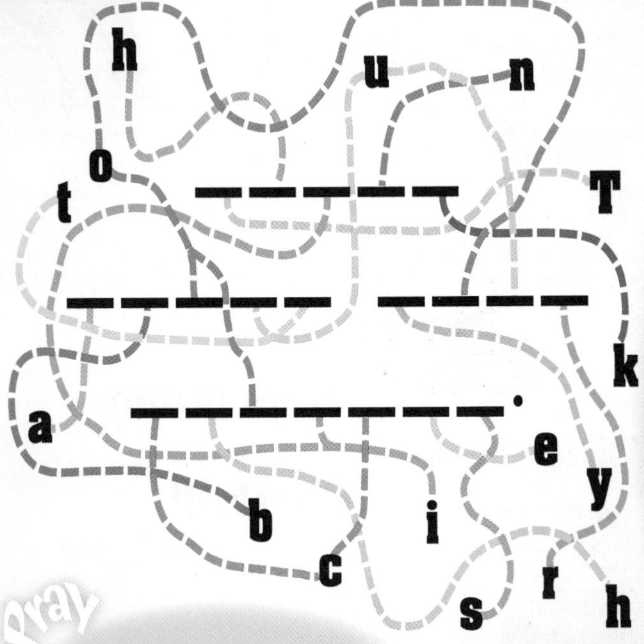

Pray
Ask God to help you obey today.

SATURDAY Malachi 3:16

God is all-knowing. He knows what you talk about with your friends.

Put a smiley face by the statements that make God glad. Put a frown by the statements that make God sad.

Let's invite Elissa to play with us.

Can I copy your homework before school?

I don't like our teacher. Do you?

I'm going to church tomorrow. Are you?

Let's hide from Alexis so we don't have to play with her.

Pray
Tell God you want your words to make Him happy.

COMMENT CORNER

Parent or Leader, circle a comment and/or write your own.

You're special · You can do it · God loves you! · Nice job! · We're proud of you! · Keep it up · WOW!

DAYS COMPLETED

WEEK 18

"Crazy Costumes"

SUNDAY John 1:1

You have different names also. Write the name that each person could call you.

Dad: s o n

Sibling: ___ ___ ___ ___ ___ ___ ___

Teacher: ___ ___ ___ ___ ___ ___ ___

Coach: ___ ___ ___ ___ ___ ___

Classmate: ___ ___ ___ ___ ___ ___

Student
Friend
Brother
Player

Pray Thank God for your name.

MONDAY John 1:10

When Jesus was born people did not recognize Him as God's Son.

Can you recognize these shadows? Draw a line to connect the shadows to the correct word.

dinosaur

robot

house

cat

tiger

Pray Tell God you recognize His Son is Jesus.

TUESDAY John 1:14

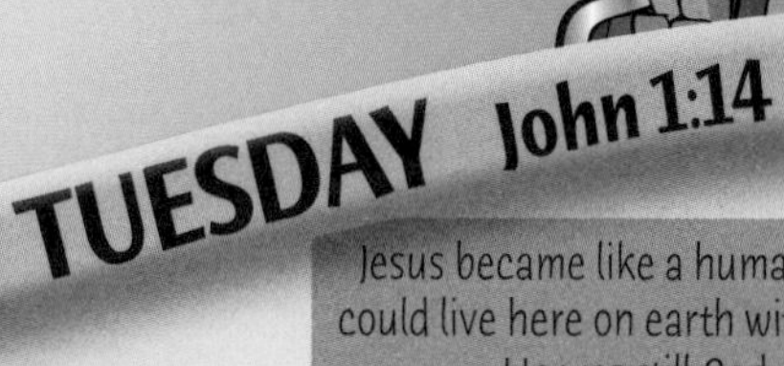

When you put on a costume you change the way you look, but not who you are. Connect the costume to the name.

Superman

Cinderella

football player

rabbit

Pray Thank Jesus for coming down to earth to be born as a baby.

WEDNESDAY John 1:23

Like John, you are to tell people about Jesus.

Who can you tell? Fill in the crossword puzzle.

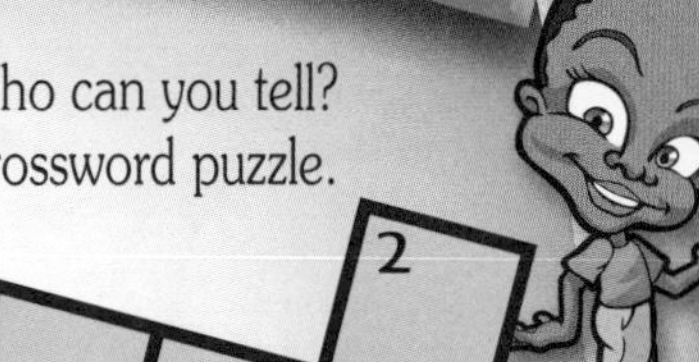

1. Another name for mom
2. Another name for classmate
3. Another name for father

Pray

Ask God to help you tell someone about Him today.

THURSDAY John 1:29

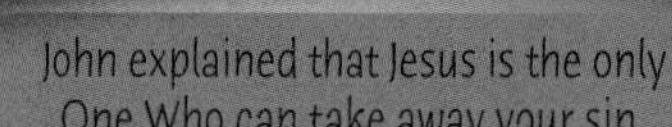

John explained that Jesus is the only One Who can take away your sin.

Write the red letters on the lines to see why Jesus came.

TSBOJPWEAGYI
LLGFFDOSRUIX
MPSQYSBHIJNO

__ ___ ___

__ ___.

Pray

Tell God thank you for sending Jesus to pay for your sin.

FRIDAY John 1:40-41

Andrew met Jesus and the first thing he did was to go tell his brother.

Insert the vowels to see Andrew's brother's name. Write the name of someone in your family that you will tell about Jesus.

i o

S__m__n

____

Pray Ask God to help you tell your family about Jesus.

SATURDAY John 1:47-48

Since Jesus is God He knew all about Nathanael before Philip introduced them.

God knows all about you also. Fill in the blanks.

He knows the color of your h_ _ _.
He hears how you talk to your p_ r_ _ t s.
He knows what you like to e_ _.
He sees what you w_ _ _ _ on T.V.

Pray

Tell God you love Him for knowing all about you.

COMMENT CORNER

Parent or Leader, circle a comment and/or write your own.

DAYS COMPLETED

You're special · You can do it · God loves you! · Nice job! · We're proud of you! · Keep it up · WOW!

WEEK 19

"Hangin' with Jesus"

I love it when you guys stop by to visit with me.

Do you think Jesus likes it when we visit with Him?

Because I love you just the way you are.

Why would you like visiting with us?

I know He loves spending time with you.

Yeah, I'm hangin' with Jesus when I sing Him praise songs.

SUNDAY John 2:5

Jesus gave 2 very simple commands. Are you doing what He told you to do? Do the math.

L (8 − 2) v (10 − 5) th (8 − 3) L (10 − 4) rd,

L (9 − 3) v (6 − 1) y (7 − 1) (10 − 0) r n (7 − 2) (9 − 1) ghb (10 − 4) r.

Code: E=5, I=8, O=6, U=10

Mary gave good advice: "Do whatever He tells you."

Pray Ask God to help you love Him and others.

MONDAY John 2:19

Jesus promised that He would rise again in 3 days. The people did not understand.

Praise Jesus that He is alive! Color the picture of the empty tomb.

Pray Thank Jesus for always keeping His promises.

TUESDAY John 3:1-2

Nicodemus knew where to go when he had questions about eternal life. Where do you go when you have questions?

Match the question or activity with the correct person.

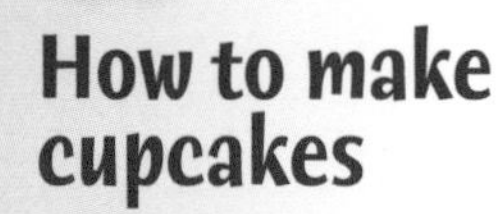

How to make cupcakes

Learning soccer rules

Solving a math equation

Building a bird house

How to go to Heaven

Pray Thank God that He has answers for your questions about Heaven.

WEDNESDAY John 3:16

John 3:16 tells the simple truth of the Bible.

Cross out all the numbers and read the sentences.

Go3d l4ov85e8s m7e2.
4G5od s2en7t J2e9sus4
7t8o d77ie 8f3or m49e3.
If9 I b45eli2eve 8in H2im,
I c7a2n l8ive2 f9ore3ver.

Pray Thank God for loving you.

THURSDAY John 3:22

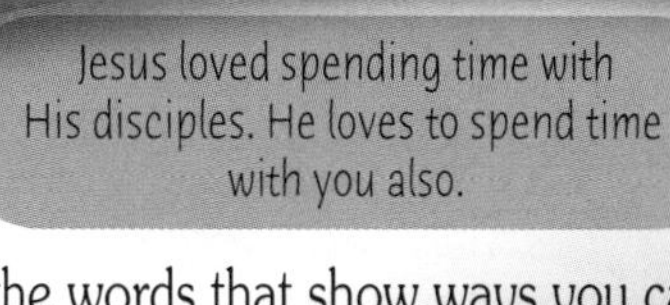

Jesus loved spending time with His disciples. He loves to spend time with you also.

Circle the words that show ways you can spend time with Jesus.

Bible
prayer
worship
songs

praise

Pray Tell Jesus that you love Him.

FRIDAY John 3:36

The Bible says if you trust Jesus as your Savior you will have eternal life.

Draw lines between the circles that match.

believes on Son
no life, wrath of God
does NOT believe in the Son.
has everlasting life

Pray Thank Jesus that He wants you to live in Heaven with Him.

SATURDAY John 4:6

Jesus knew to rest when He got tired. He was not fussy with the Samaritan woman.

It takes self-discipline to know when to work and rest. Mark each statement with an R for rest or a W for work.

___**Time out (basketball)**
___**Study spelling words**
___**Base (tag)**
___**your bed**
___**Play computer**
___**Memorize Bible verses**

Pray Ask God to help you know when you need to rest.

COMMENT CORNER

Parent or Leader, circle a comment and/or write your own.

DAYS COMPLETED

You're special
You can do it
God loves you!
Nice job!
We're proud of you!
Keep it up
WOW!

WEEK 20

SUNDAY John 4:29

The Samaritan woman invited people, even her enemies, to come meet Jesus.

You want your friends to go to Heaven, but what about the boy or girl who is not nice to you? Write the name of one person who is unkind to you and pray that they will meet Jesus. Ask God how you can show them His love.

For God so loved ...

_______________________________________ **John 3:16**

Pray Ask God to help you be kind to someone who is mean to you.

MONDAY John 4:37

Working together to tell your friends about Jesus is teamwork. Ask others to work with you to witness to your friends.

Write the name of a friend from each group that you could teamwork with for Jesus.

School friend_______________________

Neighborhood friend_______________________

Sport/club friend_______________________

Pray Tell God you will work with others to show His love.

TUESDAY John 4:50

The man with the sick son took Jesus at His word. He did not argue with Him.

When your parents tell you something, do you take them at their word or argue? Find the 3 letters hidden in the picture to see what God calls arguing.

Pray Ask God to help you obey and not argue today.

WEDNESDAY John 5:6

Jesus gave the man a choice. He gives you choices, too.

If you want to make good choices you need to ask Jesus for help. Write the name of someone who could help you with each task.

Study for test: ____________

Make a goal: ____________

Clean up your room: ____________

Make good choices: ____________

Bake cookies: ____________

Teammates Grandmother Dad Jesus Mom

Pray Tell Jesus you want His help in making good choices.

THURSDAY John 5:18

Jesus said He was God's Son. This makes Him equal to God.

God the Father and God the Son are =. Do the math. Draw a line between the answers that are =.

2 + 8 = _	10 - 3 = _
10 - 4 = _	7 + 3 = _
3 + 4 = _	8 - 2 = _

Pray Thank God for sharing His Son Jesus with you.

FRIDAY John 5:19

Jesus copies what He sees God doing.

If your friends copied what you do, what would they be doing? Put a P for pleasing God or a S for sinning in front of each statement.

__lying

__showing kindness

__obeying the first time

__tattling

__hitting

__telling the truth

Pray Tell Jesus you want to copy His good choices.

SATURDAY John 5:36

God gave Jesus a job to do and He did it.

God has given you jobs to do also. Are you doing them? Fill in the circles with vowels to complete the words.

H○n○r G○d ○nd h○n○r p○r○nts.

a e o

Pray Tell God you will do your job like Jesus did His job.

COMMENT CORNER

Parent or Leader, circle a comment and/or write your own.

You're special · You can do it · God loves you! · Nice job! · We're proud of you! · Keep it up · WOW!

DAYS COMPLETED

WEEK 21

"Read the Directions"

SUNDAY John 6:11

1) Person who _ _ _ _ _ the food.

2) Delivers your meal to the table.

3) Person who washes the _ _ _ _ _ _.

cooks dishes server

In addition to God, who else can you thank for your food? Fill in the answers.

Jesus gave thanks to God before He ate His food. Do you?

Pray

Today tell God your favorite food. Thank Him for it.

MONDAY John 6:19

Jesus showed that He was God by performing miracles. Walking on water is a miracle.

Healing is also a miracle. Find and circle the body parts listed in the Bible that Jesus healed.

EARS EYES HANDS LEGS MOUTH

X	W	I	C	L	L	E	G	S
R	Z	G	A	M	N	A	R	H
H	A	N	D	S	O	U	E	P
D	G	P	X	B	E	Y	E	S
A	E	M	O	U	T	H	T	S
R	B	N	W	G	M	O	P	D
L	Z	M	X	E	A	R	S	A

Pray

Thank God for the powers He gave Jesus.

TUESDAY John 6:24

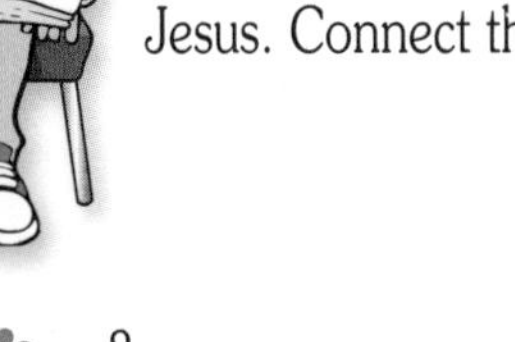

The people went searching for Jesus. Where do you look for information on Jesus?

There is only one place to get true answers about Jesus. Connect the dots. Have you read it today?

Pray

Ask God to help you remember to look in your Bible to learn about Jesus.

WEDNESDAY John 6:40

The plan is simple. Jesus accepts everyone who comes to Him.

Cross out the people who cannot come to Jesus.

Basketball players
Cheaters
Pastors
Liars
People in wheelchairs
Poor people
Students who get A's
Children
Thieves

Pray Ask God to help you love everyone like He does.

THURSDAY John 6:42

The Jews only knew Jesus as Mary's son. Jesus explained that He was also God's Son that came down from Heaven.

Who told Mary and Joseph that Jesus was God's Son? Write the first letter of each picture to find the answer.

___ ___ ___ ___ ___

Pray Thank God that He is Jesus' Father.

FRIDAY John 6:52

The Jews argued among themselves when they didn't understand Jesus' words. Jesus explained His words to them.

Do you argue with your friends when you disagree? Draw a line to connect the problem to the correct book.

Cookbook
Bible

What is a home run?
How to spell a word correctly?
Who is Jesus?
How to bake a cake?

Rule book
Dictionary

Pray Thank God for one person who helps you understand.

SATURDAY John 6:64

Because Jesus is God He knows what you are thinking. Some people said they loved Jesus, but on the inside they did not.

Your actions might show that you love Jesus, but God sees your heart. Color the heart red if you love Jesus on the inside.

Pray Ask God to help you love Jesus from the inside out.

COMMENT CORNER

Parent or Leader, circle a comment and/or write your own.

You're special · You can do it · God loves you! · Nice job! · We're proud of you! · Keep it up · WOW!

DAYS COMPLETED

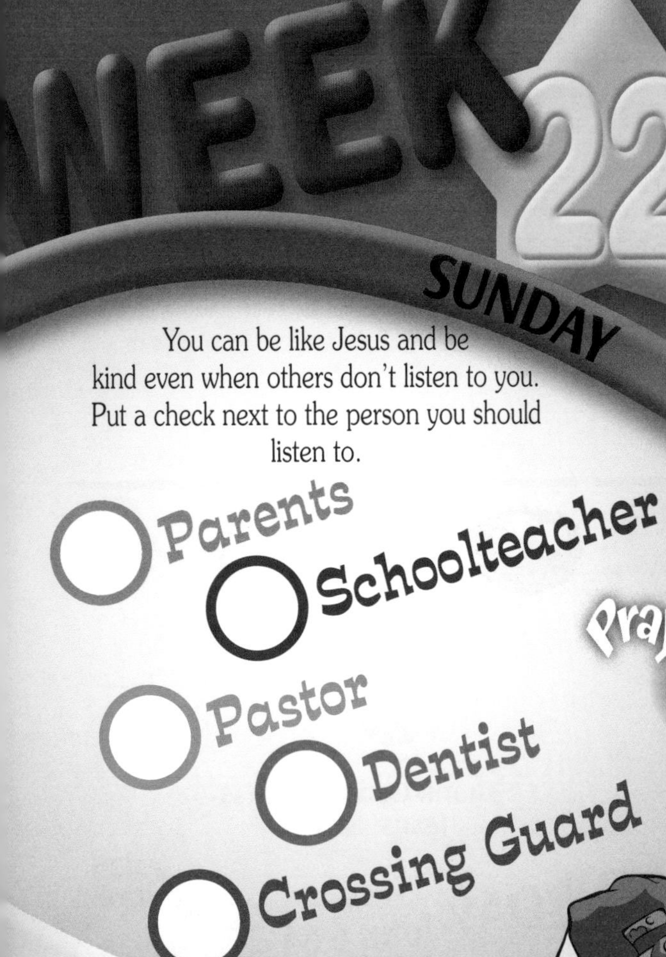

WEEK 22

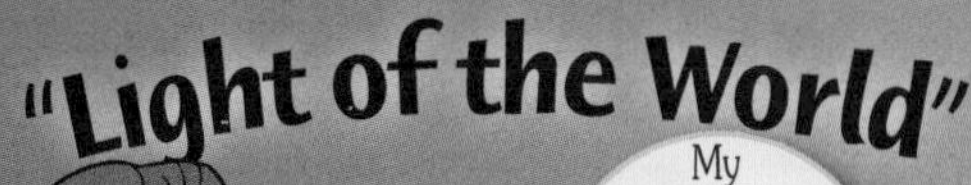

"Light of the World"

SUNDAY John 7:5

You can be like Jesus and be kind even when others don't listen to you. Put a check next to the person you should listen to.

- ◯ Parents
- ◯ Schoolteacher
- ◯ Pastor
- ◯ Dentist
- ◯ Crossing Guard

Pray Ask God to help you be like Jesus and not argue.

MONDAY John 7:14

Jesus taught what He knew about God to others. You can teach your friends about God.

Fill in the consonants to find stories you could share.

a◯i◯ and Goliath

Jesus ◯a◯◯e◯ on water.

Jesus died on the ◯◯o◯◯.

◯e◯u◯ rose again.

Pray Ask God to help you tell His story.

TUESDAY John 7:29

Jesus said that God sent Him to the world. Jesus obeyed God.

Do you obey God? Put a check besides the commandments that you choose to obey.

- ◯ Love God more than TV.
- ◯ Remember to go to church.
- ◯ Obey your parents.
- ◯ Do not say the word "God" unless you are talking to or about Him.
- ◯ Do not hate your enemies.
- ◯ Do not tell lies.

Pray Tell God you want to be like Jesus and choose to obey.

WEDNESDAY John 7:30

Jesus would have allowed the soldiers to arrest Him, but it was not yet time for this.

Jesus is always in control. Nothing happens without His permission. Find and circle the items Jesus controls.

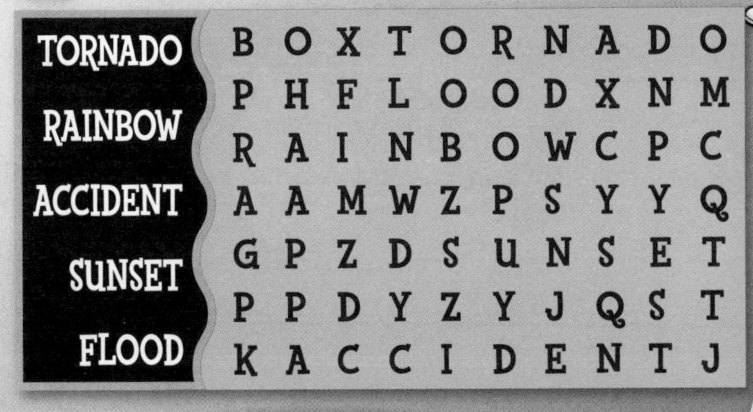

TORNADO	B	O	X	T	O	R	N	A	D	O
RAINBOW	P	H	F	L	O	O	D	X	N	M
ACCIDENT	R	A	I	N	B	O	W	C	P	C
SUNSET	A	A	M	W	Z	P	S	Y	Y	Q
FLOOD	G	P	Z	D	S	U	N	S	E	T
	P	P	D	Y	Z	Y	J	Q	S	T
	K	A	C	C	I	D	E	N	T	J

Pray Ask Jesus to help you trust Him to take care of you even when bad things happen.

THURSDAY John 7:40-41

People in Bible times did not understand that Jesus is God's Son. Even people today do not understand.

Write the first letter of each answer to know where to find the truth about Jesus.

B ___ ___ ___ ___
1 2 3 4 5

1) Round item you play sports with
2) Another word for "me"
3) Has two wheels and a seat, maybe even a bell
4) You turn it on to read
5) It comes from a chicken or duck

Pray Tell Jesus that you know that He is God's Son.

FRIDAY John 8:7

Jesus said you should be busy asking God to forgive you for your sin instead of telling on your friends. Everybody sins.

Write two sins you need to ask God to forgive you for today.

Pray Tell God about two bad choices you made today.

SATURDAY John 8:12

Jesus said He is the Light of the world. Light shows us where to go when it is dark.

Write the light that goes with each word.

1) On a car ________light
2) In your bedroom __________light
3) On a road _____________ light
4) By your front door __________ light
5) In your hand __________light

flash
head
night
porch
street

Pray Thank God for sending Jesus to be our Light to get to Heaven.

COMMENT CORNER

Parent or Leader, circle a comment and/or write your own.

You're special · You can do it · God loves you! · Nice job! · We're proud of you! · Keep it up · WOW!

DAYS COMPLETED

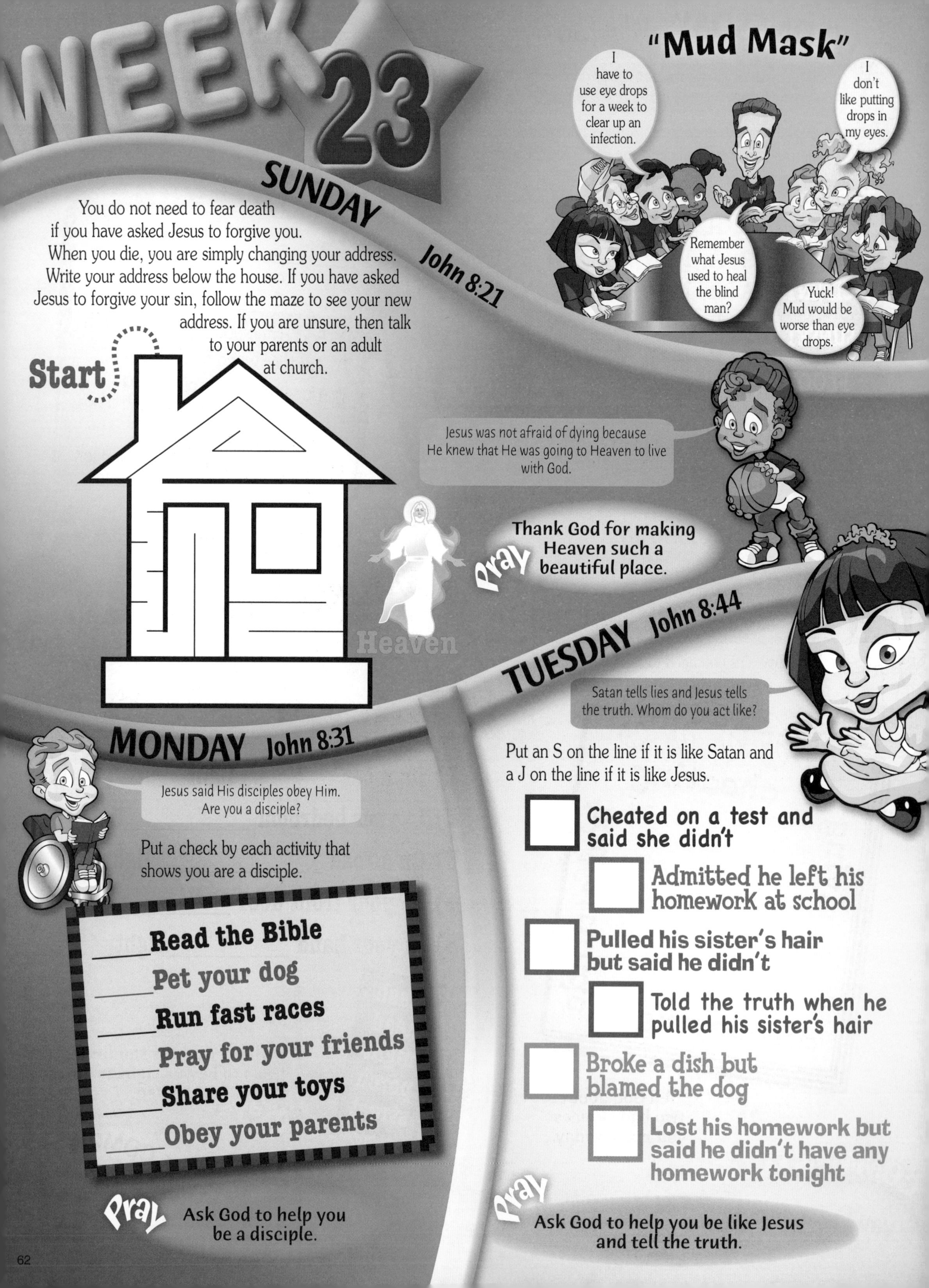

WEEK 23
"Mud Mask"
I have to use eye drops for a week to clear up an infection.
I don't like putting drops in my eyes.
Remember what Jesus used to heal the blind man?
Yuck! Mud would be worse than eye drops.
SUNDAY John 8:21
You do not need to fear death if you have asked Jesus to forgive you. When you die, you are simply changing your address. Write your address below the house. If you have asked Jesus to forgive your sin, follow the maze to see your new address. If you are unsure, then talk to your parents or an adult at church.
Start
Heaven
Jesus was not afraid of dying because He knew that He was going to Heaven to live with God.
Pray Thank God for making Heaven such a beautiful place.
MONDAY John 8:31
Jesus said His disciples obey Him. Are you a disciple?
Put a check by each activity that shows you are a disciple.
____ Read the Bible
____ Pet your dog
____ Run fast races
____ Pray for your friends
____ Share your toys
____ Obey your parents
Pray Ask God to help you be a disciple.
TUESDAY John 8:44
Satan tells lies and Jesus tells the truth. Whom do you act like?
Put an S on the line if it is like Satan and a J on the line if it is like Jesus.
Cheated on a test and said she didn't
Admitted he left his homework at school
Pulled his sister's hair but said he didn't
Told the truth when he pulled his sister's hair
Broke a dish but blamed the dog
Lost his homework but said he didn't have any homework tonight
Pray Ask God to help you be like Jesus and tell the truth.

WEDNESDAY John 8:58

Before Jesus was born in Bethlehem, He was alive in Heaven. Since Jesus is God He has no beginning or ending.

Fill in your beginning day (birthday) on the lines. Remember that Jesus has no beginning and no ending days.

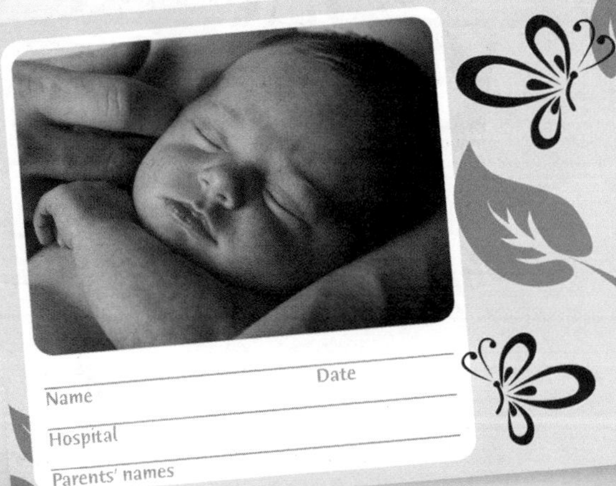

Pray Thank God that Jesus has always been alive.

THURSDAY John 9:11

Jesus used mud to heal a man's eyesight. The mud was not magical. Jesus healed him because of the man's belief.

Number the pictures in the order they happened.

Pray Thank Jesus for healing the blind man.

FRIDAY John 9:15

Witnessing is simply telling what Jesus has done for you. What can you tell about Jesus?

Fill in the blanks to see things you can tell about Jesus.

ACROSS
2) He keeps me calm on the ______ field.
3) He _______ my sins.
4) He makes me brave at the ______'s office.

DOWN
1) He helps me remember my spelling _____.
2) He comforts me when I am ______.

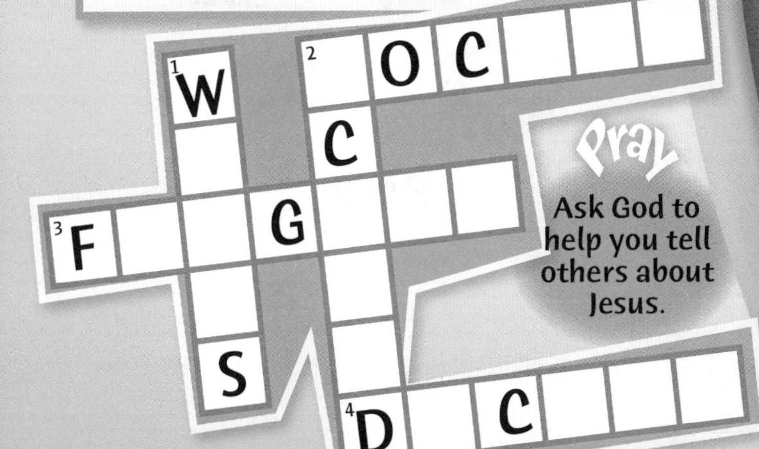

Pray Ask God to help you tell others about Jesus.

SATURDAY John 9:33

The healed man said Jesus got His power from God. Where do you get your power to do good?

Cross out the numbers and write the letters in order. Circle the correct answer.

C5er78eal _______
3Spi4nach _______
G774od2 ___
9Ka55rat7e ______
M8ag4ic ____
w4an3d ____

Pray Ask God to give you power today to do good things.

COMMENT CORNER

Parent or Leader, circle a comment and/or write your own.

You're special · You can do it · God loves you! · Nice job! · We're proud of you! · Keep it up · WOW!

DAYS COMPLETED

WEEK 24

"Forever Friends"

Hey, Chris, did you tell everyone the great news?

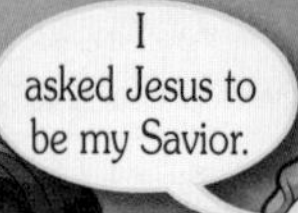

What's up, Chris?

That makes us forever friends since we will all be in Heaven together.

SUNDAY John 9:38

Fill in the vowels to see some ways to worship.

a e i o u

Ob_y
R__d th_ B_bl_
S_ng pr__s_ s_ngs
H_lp _th_rs
Incl_d_ _th_rs
Pr_y

When you believe in Jesus you want to worship Him.

Pray Use your words to tell Jesus you believe He is God's Son.

MONDAY John 10:11

A shepherd takes care of his sheep. He would protect the sheep even if it meant he died. Jesus is your shepherd. He will protect you.

Count the sheep in each group. Solve the addition problems. Circle the largest group of sheep.

5 + ____ = 8 sheep

___ + 1 = 2 sheep

___ + 1 = 3 sheep

2 + ____ = ____ sheep

Pray Thank Jesus for being your Good Shepherd.

TUESDAY John 10:14

The Good Shepherd knows all about His sheep.....you.

Write the first letter of each rhyming word to complete this sentence.

God knows what makes you

____ad, ____ad

and

____ ____ad.

Pray Tell Jesus about something that makes you mad and something that makes you glad.

WEDNESDAY John 10:28

Jesus has the power to give you eternal life if you believe in Him.

Write the correct name on each line.

Gives you an A on your spelling test

____

Gives you a hug at night

____

Gives you a library book

____

Gives you eternal life

____

Gives you a baseball uniform

____

Thank God for giving Jesus power.

THURSDAY John 10:42

After Jesus spoke, many people believed He is God's Son. What do you believe?

Circle your answer.

I believe Jesus is God's Son.

TRUE

FALSE

Pray Ask God to help you believe that Jesus is His Son.

FRIDAY John 11:5

Jesus enjoyed having friends. He cared about His friends.

How do you show your friends that you care about them? Check each answer that applies.

- ○ Invite them to church
- ○ Help them study for a test
- ○ Practice soccer with them
- ○ Be Kind to them
- ○ Invite them to sit with you at lunch
- ○ Never make fun of them

Pray Tell Jesus the names of 2 of your friends. Thank Him for your friends.

SATURDAY John 11:19

When Mary and Martha were sad they wanted to talk to Jesus.

Circle the names of people you can talk to when you are sad.

DAD FRIEND JESUS
MOM NEIGHBOR TEACHER

Y	U	O	Q	U	D	R	D	A	D
P	H	J	V	O	H	O	G	O	T
M	O	M	Q	J	E	S	U	S	Q
M	F	R	I	E	N	D	S	R	M
P	H	F	T	J	I	T	Z	A	G
A	L	W	T	E	A	C	H	E	R
N	E	I	G	H	B	O	R	P	O

Pray Thank Jesus for listening to you when you are sad.

COMMENT CORNER

Parent or Leader, circle a comment and/or write your own.

You're special · You can do it · God loves you! · Nice job! · We're proud of you!

WOW!

DAYS COMPLETED

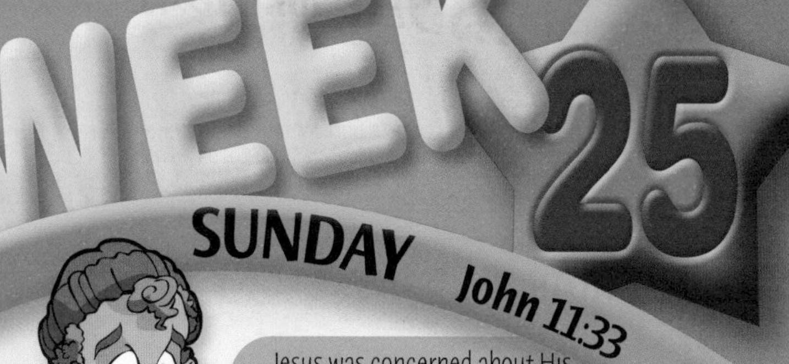

WEEK 25

"Thanks 4 Listening"

My mom had to go out of town this week. I really miss her.
I'm sure she is missing you, too.
Maybe your dad will let you call her tonight.
You are great friends. Thanks for listening.
You can tell us about your game. We will listen.

SUNDAY John 11:33

Jesus was concerned about His friends because they were very sad. How can you show compassion to your friends?

Do the math to find the answer.

8	10	5	7	3	8
-3	-2	+5	-3	+4	-6
___	___	___	___	___	___

E=7 I=8 L=5
N=2 S=10 T=4

Pray

Ask God to help you be a friend that has good listening ears.

MONDAY John 11:44

Jesus said thank you to God for listening to Him.

Whom do you thank for listening to you? Write down 3 people that listen to you.

1. ______________________

2. ______________________

3. ______________________

Pray

Tell God the names of 3 people who listen to you.

TUESDAY John 11:53

Some people were not happy when Jesus did good things. People may not like you when you do good things.

You have a choice to make. Check which decision you will make.

Do good even if I lose some friends

Do bad so my friends will like me

Pray

Tell God you will make good choices even if your friends get mad.

WEDNESDAY John 12:6

Sometimes it can be hard to be happy for your friend when she gets what you wanted.

Put a check next to the times you can be happy for a friend.

- when my friend gets a pet
- when my friend gets an A on a spelling test
- at my friend's birthday party
- when my friend gets picked for a team
- when my friend goes on vacation

Pray

Ask God to help you be a good friend.

THURSDAY John 12:15

God told Zechariah that Jesus would ride a donkey colt into Jerusalem, hundreds of years before it happened.

Match the animal to their baby.

Donkey	Eaglet
Cat	Polliwog
Seal	Cub
Bear	Pup
Butterfly	Colt
Eagle	Caterpillar
Goat	Kitten
Frog	Kid

Pray

Thank God for your mommy.

FRIDAY John 12:21

Some men went to Philip to ask him if they could meet Jesus.

What would you do if someone asked you how to meet Jesus? Follow the lines to see one answer.

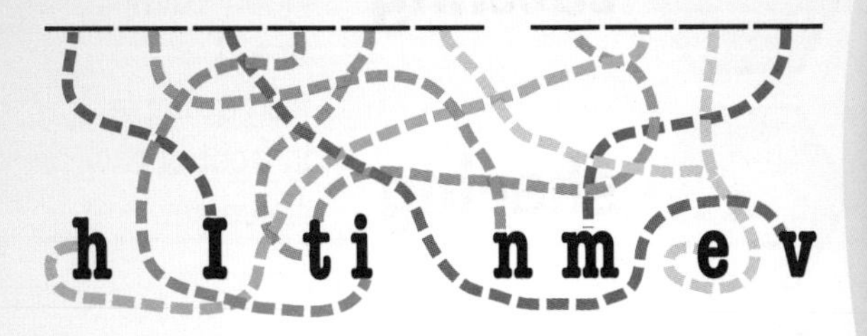

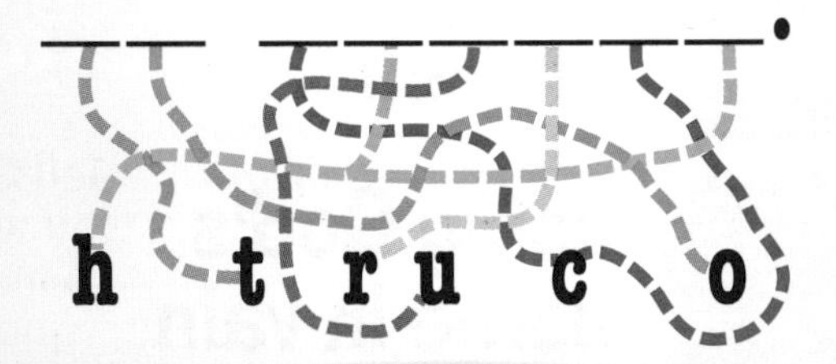

Pray

Thank God for your pastor.

SATURDAY John 12:27

Jesus chose to do a hard thing to bring glory to His Father, God.

Sometimes you will have to choose. Will you bring glory to your Heavenly Father by obeying Him? Check your answer.

Yes, I will ask Jesus to help me.

Pray

Tell God one thing that is hard for you to do. Ask Him to help you.

COMMENT CORNER

Parent or Leader, circle a comment and/or write your own.

You're special | You can do it | God loves you! | Nice job! | We're proud of you! | Keep it up | WOW!

DAYS COMPLETED

WEEK 26

"Love In Action"

What happened?

We were having a race today at recess and I fell down.

They were showing love in action.

Yeah, they could have won the race, but they cared for you instead.

Paul and Andy stopped to help me up.

SUNDAY John 12:49

God has commandments for you, too. Will you choose to obey like Jesus? Put a T before each true commandment from the Bible.

God commanded Jesus what to do. Jesus had to decide if He was going to obey or not.

Tell God you will choose to obey like Jesus did.

- ☐ Drink milk for breakfast
- ☐ Obey your parents
- ☐ Read your Bible
- ☐ Never wear blue shoes
- ☐ Love others as you love yourself

MONDAY John 13:5

Jesus took care of His friends. He did the dirty job no one else wanted to do.

Do you show love for others by doing things for them or helping them? Put a check next to the things you can do to show you care for your friends.

- ○ Help tie my friend's shoe
- ○ Help my friend with their chores
- ○ Help my friend study their spelling words
- ○ Invite my friend to play with me at recess

Ask God to help you be a good friend.

TUESDAY John 13:15

Jesus told His friends that He was their example. They could do what He did and be making good choices. Are you a good example to your friends?

Put a G (good example) or a B (bad example) in front of each statement.

- tattling
- sharing
- going to church
- using God's name in vain
- obeying the first time
- wearing your seat belt

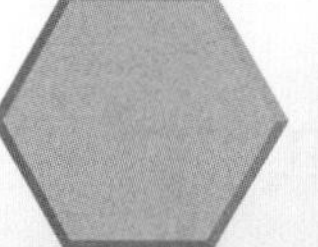

Tell God you want to make good choices for your friends to follow.

WEDNESDAY John 13:21

Jesus knows your thoughts. Does that make your happy or embarrass you?

Fill in the missing blanks. Circle the thought that would make Jesus proud of you.

Pray

Ask God to help you have good thoughts.

THURSDAY John 13:35

Jesus says that believers will be known by the love they show to each other.

Unscramble the words to see ways to show love to your friends.

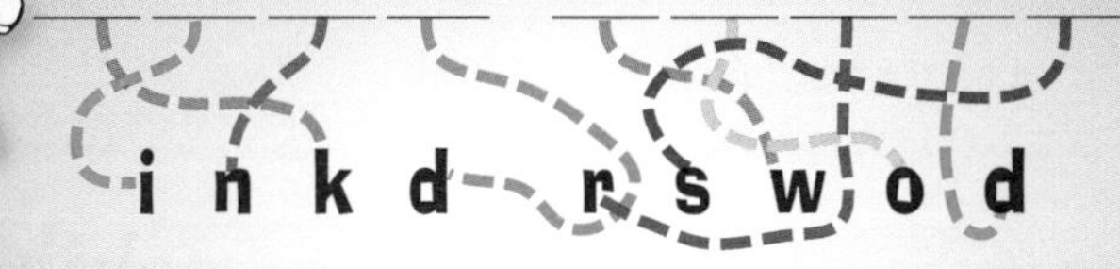

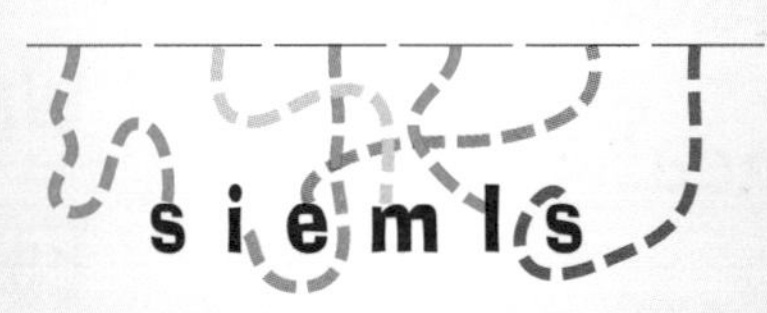

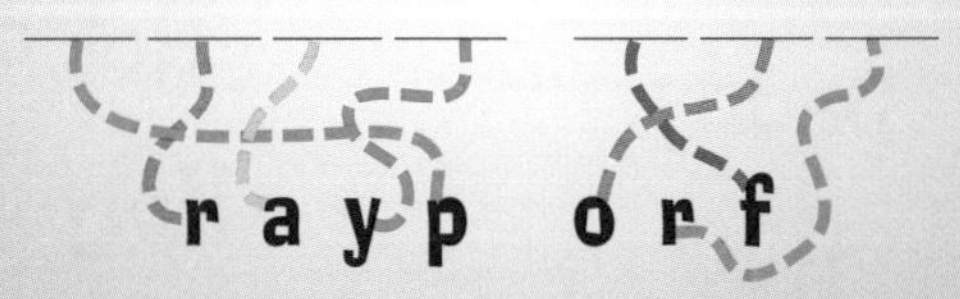

Pray Ask God to help you show love today to a friend.

FRIDAY John 14:2

Jesus is the best friend you can have. He is preparing a home for you in Heaven.

How do you get to this home? Work the crossword to find out.

1) _ _ _ _ Jesus you are sorry for your sins, bad choices.

2) Ask Him to _ _ _ _ _ _ _ your sins.

Pray

Ask God to help you tell your friends about Heaven.

SATURDAY John 14:12

Jesus told the disciples that He was going to Heaven.

Write the letters to see one thing Jesus is doing in Heaven.

Start

P 7 r e 9 p 7 a r i n 5 g a h 3 o m 6 e f 0 3 6 r 4 y o u 4

_ _ _ _ _ _ _ _ _

_ _ _ _ _

_ _ _ _ _ _

Pray

Thank Jesus that Heaven is a real place.

COMMENT CORNER

Parent or Leader, circle a comment and/or write your own.

You're special · You can do it · God loves you! · Nice job! · We're proud of you! · Keep it up · WOW!

DAYS COMPLETED

WEEK 27

"Holy Spirit Calling"

Today when I talked back to my mom, I could hear this little voice in my head.....

That is the Holy Spirit letting you know that you are sinning.

That happened to me to when I lied about my homework.

I hear it when I ye at my baby sister.

Draw a line between the words that mean the same thing.

Counselor	Automobiles
Pancake	Water
Cars	Father
Daddy	Hot cake
H2O	Holy Spirit

SUNDAY John 14:16

Counselor is another word for the Holy Spirit. Jesus said the Counselor would be with you forever. A counselor helps you make good decisions.

Pray

Ask the Holy Spirit to help you make good decisions.

MONDAY John 14:26

When you hear that little voice in your head reminding you to obey, that is the Holy Spirit talking to you. Jesus said the Holy Spirit would remind you to do what's right.

Fill in the consonants to see one of the Holy Spirit's jobs.

d g h J m n
R s t w y

_e_i_ _ _ou
_ _a_ _e_u_
_au_ _ _.

Pray

Thank God for sending the Holy Spirit to help you remember.

TUESDAY John 15:5

Jesus said that in order to make good choices you will need His help.

Where can you learn how to make good choices? Mark out all the numbers to find the hidden word. Write it on the line.

12575B8901426B85389L467134E

____

Pray

Tell Jesus that you need His help to make good choices.

WEDNESDAY John 15:15

Jesus calls you His friend. He said that He told you everything He learned about His Father, God.

Who do you call friend? Have you told them about God? Write their name and put a check by it if you have told them about Jesus.

Pray Thank Jesus for being your friend.

THURSDAY John 16:8

A bad choice makes you feel sad; a good choice makes you feel happy. The Holy Spirit wants you to tell Jesus you are sorry when you make bad choices.

Draw a happy face next to the good choices. Draw a sad face next to the bad choices.

- Share my candy with my friend.
- Obey when my dad tells me to pick up my toys.
- Tell the new boy in class that I do not want to play with him.
- Copy off my classmate's test.
- Help clean my Sunday school room after class.

Pray Ask Jesus to help you be quick to say that you are sorry when you make a bad choice.

FRIDAY John 16:20

The people would be sad when Jesus died on the cross. They would be happy when He came alive from the grave.

Write these words next to their opposites.

old, empty, dry, girl, slow

wet ____________

boy ____________

fast ____________

full ____________

new ____________

Pray Tell God you are happy Jesus rose from the dead.

SATURDAY John 16:32

Jesus knew what it was like to be lonely. All His friends left Him, but He knew that God would never leave Him.

What can you do when you are lonely? Find the words in the word search.

BICYCLE
BUILD
DRAW
PRAY
READ
WRITE

L	B	I	C	Y	C	L	E	S	V
O	N	R	M	E	S	Z	K	Z	R
S	A	G	H	B	U	I	L	D	F
P	K	P	R	A	Y	C	P	X	K
P	F	M	E	B	R	E	A	D	T
G	Y	D	R	A	W	R	I	T	E
G	J	Z	B	P	U	G	F	E	M

Pray Thank God that He is always there for you.

COMMENT CORNER

Parent or Leader, circle a comment and/or write your own.

You're special · You can do it · God loves you! · Nice job! · We're proud of you! · Keep it up · WOW!

DAYS COMPLETED

WEEK 28

"Get in Position"

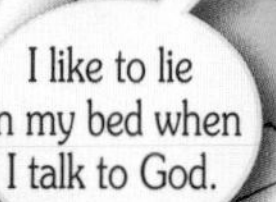
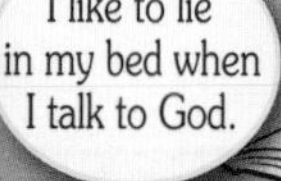

SUNDAY John 17:1

Prayer is simply communicating with God. Unscramble the words to find ways that you communicate with friends.

In a l _ _ t _ r **tterle**

On the c _ m _ _ t _ r **putcomer**

Using the _ h _ n _ **oephn**

Face to _ _ c _ **ecaf**

Pray Thank God that He loves hearing from you—eyes open or shut.

MONDAY John 17:24

Jesus said that even before the world was created, He was with God. We celebrate when Jesus was born on earth, but He was alive before the earth was here.

Write what comes before.

__, 4, 6, 8

________, cat, puppy, dog

________, grandma, man, grandpa

__,2, 3, 4

Pray

Thank God that before the world was created Jesus was alive.

TUESDAY John 18:1

Jesus prayed when He had hard things to do. God gave Him power to do what He had to do.

Connect each word to its power source.

car

sailboat

lamp

remote control car

electrical socket

wind

gas pump

batteries

Pray

Ask God to give you power to do good.

WEDNESDAY John 18:17

Peter lied. Lying is a sin. Grown-ups sin. Children sin. The Bible says everyone sins.

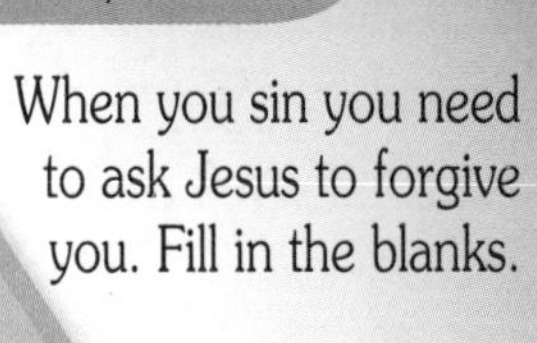

When you sin you need to ask Jesus to forgive you. Fill in the blanks.

Who sins?

E _ e _ y _ n _.

Who needs to ask for forgiveness?

_ v _ r _ o _ e

Pray

Ask God to help you ask for forgiveness after you sin.

Have you asked Jesus to forgive your sins?

Yes/No

THURSDAY John 18:40

The Jews chose the criminal, Barabbas, over Jesus.

Circle the things that you sometimes choose over Jesus.

selfishness

hurtful words

bad attitude

disobedience

Pray

Ask God to help you make good choices.

FRIDAY John 19:3

The Roman soldiers hurt Jesus with their hands.

Do you hurt Jesus with your words? Put a check beside the words that would hurt Jesus, if you said them to someone.

__I don't like you.

__Want to come play with me?

__You are too slow to run with me.

__Yuck, that tastes terrible.

__I don't want to share.

__I will slow down so we can run together.

__No, thank you.

Pray

Ask God to help you say kind words.

SATURDAY John 19:12

Pilate was afraid to do the right thing. He was afraid of what people would say about him.

Whom do you want to please more? Circle ◯ your answer.

Pray

Tell God you want to do the right thing.

COMMENT CORNER

Parent or Leader, circle a comment and/or write your own.

You're special · You can do it · God loves you! · Nice job! · We're proud of you! · Keep it up · WOW!

DAYS COMPLETED

WEEK 29

"Seeing is Believing"

Why do you think that? Did you see them?

I think new neighbors moved in across the street from me.

No, the For Rent sign is gone and I saw a moving truck.

And there were lights on there last night.

What you have seen points to new neighbors, even if you haven't seen them.

SUNDAY John 19:30

Write the first letter of each picture on the line to see why Jesus chose to die.

O__ __y _i_

__ __oo_ _ou__ __

_ay _o_ you_ _i_.

Jesus chose to die. The Roman soldiers would not have killed Him if He had not allowed it.

Pray Thank Jesus that He died for you.

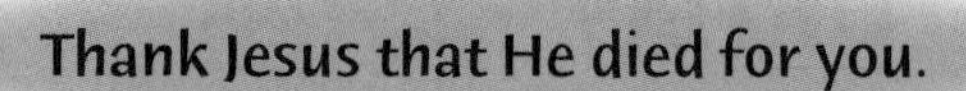

MONDAY John 19:32

His testimony is true. This man was known to always tell the truth.

Do you always tell the truth? Put a check beside the times it is hard to tell the truth.

- When I break the glass.
- When I don't brush my teeth.
- When I hit my sister.
- When I don't eat my lunch.
- When I say a bad word.

Pray Ask Jesus to help you always tell the truth.

TUESDAY John 20:8

The disciple saw and believed. What kind of things help you believe?

Find the words in the word search that help you believe in God.

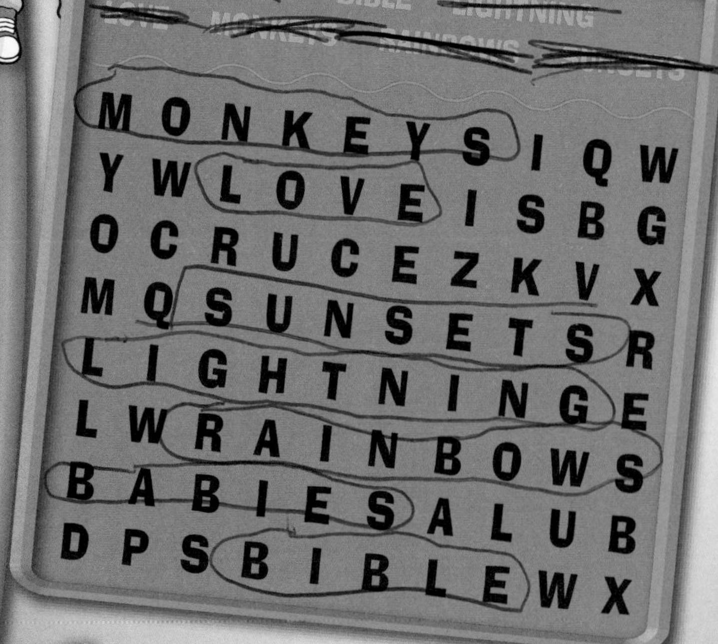

Pray Thank God for showing Himself to you in creation.

WEDNESDAY John 20:15

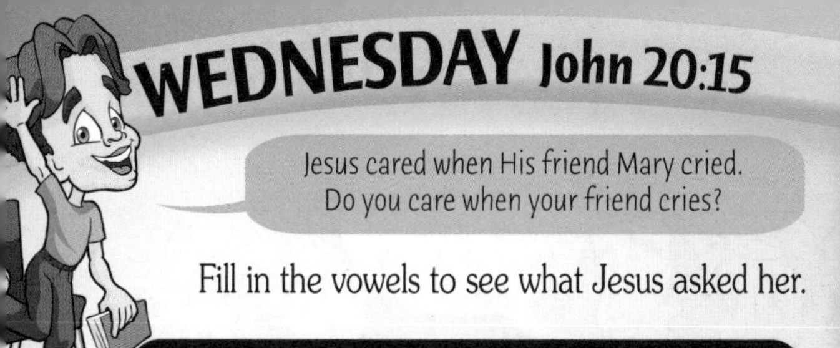

Jesus cared when His friend Mary cried. Do you care when your friend cries?

Fill in the vowels to see what Jesus asked her.

a e i o u y

Pray Ask God to help you care for your friends like Jesus cared for Mary.

THURSDAY John 20:31

The Bible was given to you from God so that you would believe in Him.

The Bible is the most important book. Fill in a letter for the missing numbers to see what you should do with it.

49,__,51 28,29,__ __11,12 19,__,21 and

__,41,42 69,__,71 29,__,31 59,__,61.

Code: A=10, B=70, D=20, E=30, O=40, R=50, Y=60

Pray Thank God for giving you the Bible.

FRIDAY John 21:6, 11

Jesus told the fisherman how to catch fish. They chose to obey Him.

Count the fish by 10s to see how many fish they caught.

___ Fish

+___ Fish

+ 3 Fish

___ Fish

Pray Ask God to help you obey like the disciples did.

SATURDAY John 21: 17

Jesus knows all things. He knows that you love Him, but He wants to hear you say it.

Color the picture and then tell it to Jesus.

I LOVE YOU JESUS!

Pray Tell Jesus you love Him.

COMMENT CORNER Parent or Leader, circle a comment and/or write your own.

You're special · You can do it · God loves you! · Nice job! · We're proud of you! · Keep it up · WOW!

DAYS COMPLETED

SUNDAY Romans 1:4

Jesus Christ rose from the dead. He is living today, and He wants to be your Savior from sin.

Color the picture. Isn't it wonderful that you can know that Jesus is alive? Hallelujah!

Pray Thank Jesus for loving you.

MONDAY Romans 1:8

Paul was thankful to God for his friends in Rome. He was glad that they were known around the world for their faith. You can be known for your faith in God, too.

Use the color code key to find the hidden word.

1=blue 2=yellow 3=red

Pray Thank God that you can have faith in Him.

TUESDAY Romans 1:22

People sometimes think they are wiser than God. When this happens, they really show that they are not wise at all. The Bible calls these people fools. God is all-knowing. You can trust Him and His Word to help you make wise decisions.

Unscramble the word that describes what it is to think you know more than God.

Pray Tell God how thankful you are for His wisdom.

WEDNESDAY Romans 2:2

God judges you according to truth. You can find truth in His Word, the Bible. The Bible helps you know how God wants you to live.

Follow the maze to find the word that tells what God uses to judge. Write the word in the spaces below.

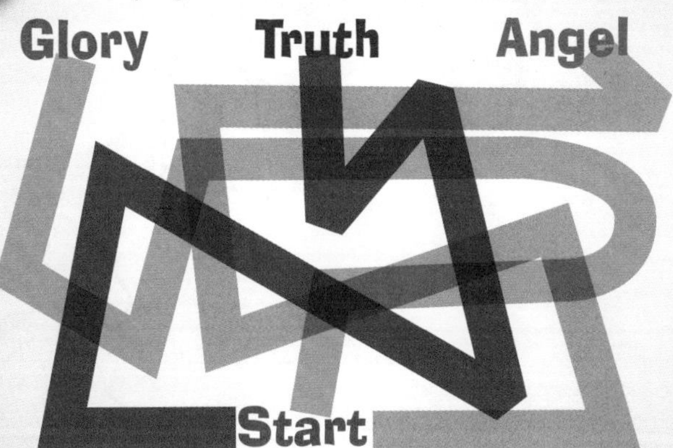

___ ___ ___ ___ ___

Pray Ask God to help you follow the truth in His Word, the Bible.

THURSDAY Romans 2:21

You should not tell others to do something if you are not doing it yourself. God wants you to be an example to others and to help them do what is right.

Write or draw one way you can be a good example today.

Good Example

Pray Ask God to help you be a good example to others today.

FRIDAY Romans 3:5-6

There may be times when you do not understand the things that are happening. You may think that God has made a mistake, but God does not make mistakes. He is perfect, and He always does what is best for you.

Circle the correct answer.

God makes mistakes.	True	or	False
God is perfect.	True	or	False
God does what is best for me.	True	or	False

Pray Thank God that you can know He will always do what is best for you.

SATURDAY Romans 3:10

The Bible tells you that no one is righteous. That means no one does the right thing every time. Everyone has sinned. God will forgive anyone who believes in Him and asks forgiveness for their sin. Then you can be right with God and you will want to do right things to please Him.

R I G H T K Y X A
K W V E H Q S I N
R I G H T E O U S
F O R G I V E B O
M J S E A W G R K

Find the words in the puzzle: **righteous, sin, forgive, right.**

Pray Thank God for making a way for you to be right with Him if you ask Him.

COMMENT CORNER Parent or Leader, circle a comment and/or write your own.

You're special · You can do it · God loves you! · Nice job! · We're proud of you! · Keep it up · WOW!

DAYS COMPLETED

WEEK 31

"A New Person"

SUNDAY Romans 3:23

Use the underlined words to fill in the blanks and complete the sentences.

The ____________ says:

Every single ___________ has sinned.

Only ___________ has never sinned.

The Bible is very clear in saying that every single person has sinned. Only God has never sinned.

Pray

Thank God for sending His Son, Jesus, to die for your sin.

MONDAY Romans 4:7

The gift of salvation from sin is the greatest gift you can ever receive.

You will never receive a greater gift than God's gift of eternal life in Heaven. It is something that you don't deserve. Talk to your parent or an adult at church to learn more. Count by twos. Write your answer in the box.

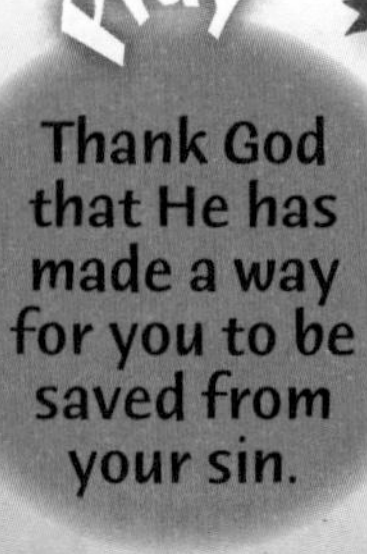

Pray

Thank God that He has made a way for you to be saved from your sin.

TUESDAY Romans 4:20

You can grow strong in faith when you believe the promises of God. Be sure to give God the glory for all He has done for you.

Write or draw a picture of something God has done for you. Have you given Him the glory and praise for this?

Pray

Praise God for what He has done for you.

WEDNESDAY Romans 5:8
God loved you so much that He sent His Son, Jesus, to die on the cross for your sin.
Fill in the circles to find the hidden message.
U
I FO
V YON .
J S D R E
Pray
Thank God for His great love for you.
THURSDAY Romans 5:21
WOL
Eternal life (living forever in Heaven) comes only through Jesus Christ. When you tell God you are sorry for your sin and ask Him to forgive you, you can know that you have eternal life.
Draw a line to Who gives eternal life.
eternal life
Start
Pray
Thank Jesus for making a way for you to have eternal life.
FRIDAY Romans 6:6
When you ask Jesus to be your Savior from sin, your life should change. Your life should now show that you want to serve God and not your sinful self. Sometimes that is not easy to do, but God promises that He will help you.
Put a checkmark next to the actions that serve God.
Obeying my parents.
Being kind to my friends.
Being a helper at church.
Taking the last piece of candy.
Not playing with my brother and sister.
Pray
Ask God to help you please Him.
SATURDAY Romans 6:23
The penalty for sin is spiritual death (not being with God in Heaven someday). God's gift of eternal life comes only through Jesus Christ. There is no other way to Heaven.
Draw a line to the correct answers:
What is the penalty for sin?
Whom does eternal life come through?
Who gave this gift?
Jesus Christ
Death
God
Pray
Thank God for loving you.
COMMENT CORNER
Parent or Leader, circle a comment and/or write your own.
DAYS COMPLETED
You're special
You can do it
God loves you!
Nice job!
We're proud of you!
Keep it up
WOW!

SUNDAY Romans 7:6

Is there a behavior or struggle that you have been working on? God will help you. Draw it in the space below. Remember to pray and ask God to help you with it.

When you have asked Jesus to be your Savior from sin, you are no longer trying to get to Heaven yourself by obeying a list of rules. God will help you as you try to live pleasing to Him.

Pray Ask God to help you with what you drew a picture of.

MONDAY Romans 7:15

Sometimes it is hard not to do what is wrong. You don't want to do wrong, but you can't seem to stop yourself. Pray and ask God for His strength to help you stop doing the wrong thing.

Circle every other word in the message below. The first word is circled for you. Write the circled words on the lines to find the hidden message.

wrong, God, things, will, sin, help, strength, you, hard, to, sometimes, do, we, what, all, is, are, right.

_____ _____

_____ _____

_____ _____ _____

_____ _____.

Pray Ask God to help you to make right choices today.

TUESDAY Romans 8:3

It is impossible to get to Heaven by being perfect. Everyone sins. God sent His Son, Jesus, as a man to be the final sacrifice for sin.

Unscramble the words to complete the sentence.

_ _ _ _ _ **is the**

s e J u s

_ _ _ _ _

n a f i l

sacrifice.

Pray Thank God for loving you.

WEDNESDAY Romans 8:15-16

If you accept the gift of salvation, you become a child of God. He adopts you into His family. He is your Heavenly Father.

Color the adoption certificate. If you are a child of God, write your name on the certificate. Talk to your parents or an adult at church if you are not sure.

is a child of God

Pray Thank God for making a way for you to be part of His family.

THURSDAY Romans 8:28

When you know God, you can know that all things work together for good. Sometimes that may be hard to understand, but you can trust God and remember this promise.

Connect the dots to see how many things work together for good when you know God.

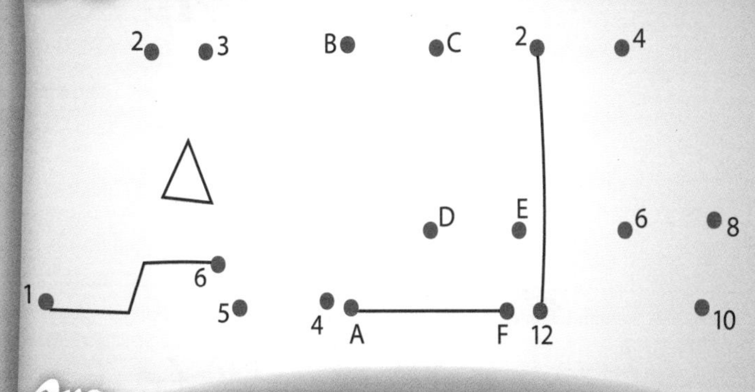

Pray Ask God to help you remember that all things work together for good.

FRIDAY Romans 9:14

God is a fair God. He makes no mistakes. His will is always right and perfect.

Solve the code to complete the message.

G___d ___s ___

f___i___ G___d.

★=a ▲=i ●=o ■=r

Pray Thank God that you can know He is always right.

SATURDAY Romans 9:17

God wants to use you to tell others about Him. Are you sharing what you are learning with others?

Put a checkmark next to the ways you can share with or tell others about God.

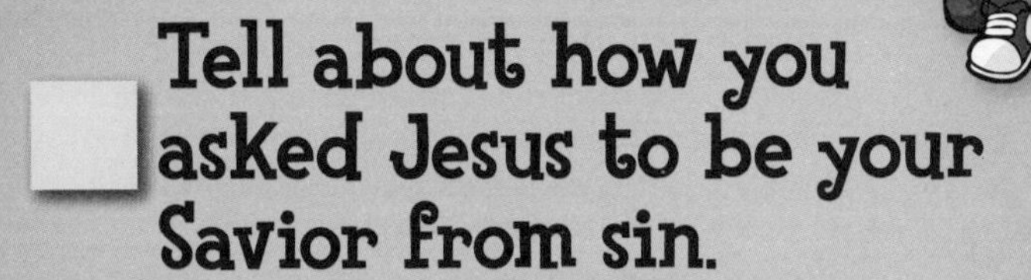

- ☐ Ignore people.
- ☐ Be rude.
- ☐ Invite a friend to church.
- ☐ Pray with your friends.

Pray Ask God to help you tell others about Him.

COMMENT CORNER

Parent or Leader, circle a comment and/or write your own.

You're special · You can do it · God loves you! · Nice job! · We're proud of you! · Keep it up · WOW!

DAYS COMPLETED

WEEK 33

"A New Family"

SUNDAY Romans 10:9

Find the 4 hidden lips in the picture.

Wow! The Bible is very clear about how to be saved from sin! If you tell God (confess) that you know Jesus died on the cross for your sin, and you believe that He came alive again, you can know that God will hear you.

Pray

Thank God that you can know for sure you are saved from sin.

MONDAY Romans 10:14

God wants others to know Him, too, but how can they know about Him if no one tells them? Do you know someone you can tell about God today? Pray and ask God to help you share what you have learned with someone else.

Draw a line from the children to the different people they can tell about God. Write the name of someone you want to tell about God on the line at the end of the maze.

Pray

Ask God to help you tell someone else about Him today.

TUESDAY Romans 11:6

Being saved from sin comes by grace alone and not by works. This means that all you have to do is accept God's gift of salvation.

Cross out the things that will not save you from sin. Circle the only way to be saved from sin.

giving money

going to church

doing kind deeds

accepting God's gift of salvation

Pray

Thank God for the gift of salvation.

WEDNESDAY Romans 11:24

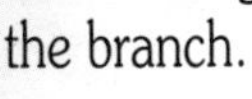

Did you know that the Bible talks about becoming grafted into God's family just like tree branches? Being grafted into God's family means that after you accept God's gift of salvation, you can grow to become more and more like Him.

Draw a new branch onto the tree and color the tree. If you have been grafted into God's family, write your name on the branch.

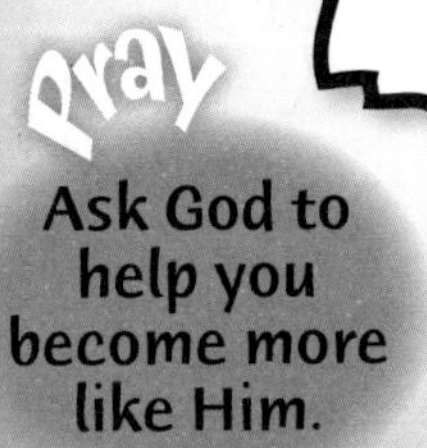

Pray Ask God to help you become more like Him.

THURSDAY Romans 11:33

God's wisdom and knowledge are more than you can even imagine. There are things about God that you will never be able to understand. How wonderful that there is nothing God does not know!

Circle T if the statement is true. Circle F if the statement is false.

God's wisdom and Knowledge are more than you can imagine. (T/F)

There are things about God you will not understand. (T/F)

There is nothing God does not Know. (T/F)

People can Know as much as God. (T/F)

Pray Thank God that He knows everything and that He cares for you.

FRIDAY Romans 12:2

God tells you not to be like the world. The world means those who have not accepted God's gift of salvation. One way you can be different from the world is by keeping your mind pure by reading God's Word, the Bible.

What did God give you to help you keep your mind pure? Add or subtract to finish the number sentences.

B	E	I	L	P
10	14	12	13	11

5	12	5	5	12
+8	-6	+5	+7	+2
-7	+3	-3	-7	-5
+4	+3	+3	+8	+5
___	___	___	___	___

Pray Ask God to help you keep your mind pure.

SATURDAY Romans 12:10

You should be kind and thoughtful to others. God wants you to show love to others by thinking about others before yourself.

Draw a heart around the things you can do to show love to others.

share with others

give time to help others

help those who need help

argue

show disrespect

Pray Ask God to help you show love to others.

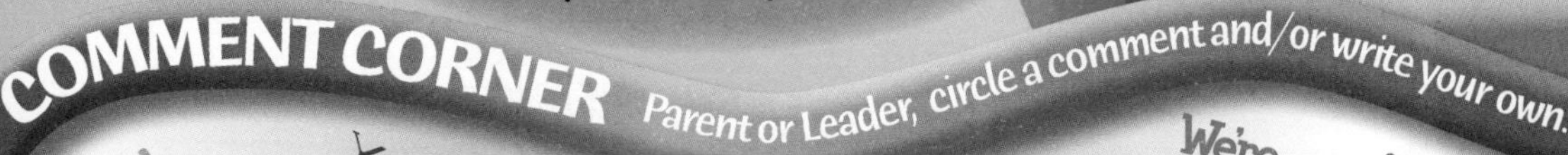

You're special

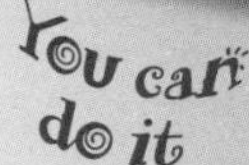

God loves you!

We're proud of you!

Keep it up

WOW!

DAYS COMPLETED

WEEK 34

"A New Way of Living"

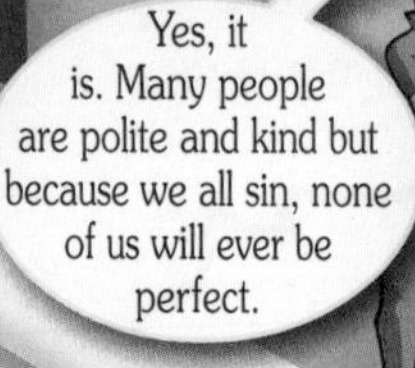

SUNDAY Romans 13:3

Write 3 good things you can do this week on the jewels. Ask God to help you with these things.

____

____

____

Do you like to be in trouble? Of course not! God says that when you do good, you will be praised and will not worry about being in trouble.

Pray Ask God to help you make the choice to do good.

MONDAY Romans 14:11

Someday every knee will bow and every tongue will praise God. That will be a wonderful day!

Color the picture of people praising Jesus and kneeling before Him.

Pray Give praise to God today.

TUESDAY Romans 14:13

God does not want you to judge others. He does not want you to do things that will cause others to do wrong. That is called being a stumbling block. God wants you to encourage others.

Circle the things that will encourage others. Cross out the things that might cause others to do wrong.

pray share

help kind words

lie

cheat

Pray Ask God to help you be an encouragement today.

WEDNESDAY Romans 15:1

God does not want you to focus on pleasing yourself. He wants you to help others, especially those who need help.

Use the word bank to fill the helping hands with people you can help.

sister
brother
mom
dad
friend
neighbor
teacher

____

____

____

____

Pray

Ask God to help you help someone else today.

THURSDAY Romans 15:30

The apostle Paul wanted the Christians in Rome to help him by praying for him. You can help others by praying for them. Can you think of someone that you can pray for today?

Write the name of the person you will pray for inside the praying hands. You will also want to add the name to your regular prayer diary. Be sure to write in your diary any answered prayers.

____

Pray

Pray for someone you know who needs encouragement today.

FRIDAY Romans 16:2

The apostle Paul asked the Christians in Rome to help his friend. You can show God's love by helping those in need today just as the Christians in the early church helped others.

Start at the arrow and write every other letter to find the hidden message.

Pray

Ask God to help you help others.

SATURDAY Romans 16:20

God is greater than Satan. He will defeat him. Go to God in prayer when you need His peace and comfort.

Who is greater than Satan? Hold your book up to a mirror to read the answer. Write the answer on the line.

____

Pray

Thank God that He is greater than Satan.

COMMENT CORNER Parent or Leader, circle a comment and/or write your own.

You're special · You can do it · God loves you! · Nice job! · We're proud of you! · Keep it up · WOW!

DAYS COMPLETED

WEEK 35

"Honoring God's Word"

SUNDAY Ezekiel 1:1

God spoke to Ezekiel in a dream. God speaks today though the Bible.

There are many ways to "hear" the Bible. Put a checkmark beside each one.

- ☐ Read the Bible
- ☐ Listen to Christian music
- ☐ Watch Christian movies
- ☐ Listen to your Sunday school teacher

Pray

Thank God for the Bible that tells you God's words.

MONDAY Ezekiel 1:28b

Ezekiel showed respect for God. When he heard God talking he bowed his head and was quiet.

You can show respect for God when you are in your classroom at church. Circle the 8 things that are different in the bottom picture.

Pray

Ask God to help you honor Him by being quiet while His Word is read.

TUESDAY Ezekiel 2:7

There are two things God wants you to do.

Go around the path clockwise. Put every letter in a square on the first line. Then go backward and write every letter in a circle on the second line.

H Y E E A B R O

_ _ _ _
and
_ _ _ _

Pray

Tell Jesus that you will tell others about Him.

WEDNESDAY Ezekiel 36:9a

God is concerned about you. He cares what happens to you.

Like God, you should be concerned about others. Cross out all of the numbers in the puzzle to discover a way to show concern for others. Write your answer on the lines.

2189n04v3i8578t2e567
o00t345h44e1r55s2745
56582t5393335760786
234c86h3u89r3436c5h6

___ ___ ___ ___ ___ ___

___ ___ ___ ___ ___ ___

___ ___

___ ___ ___ ___ ___ ___

Pray Thank God for caring about you.

THURSDAY Ezekiel 36:19

God judges your actions whether they are good or bad.

Draw a line from the action to the correct word.

sharing

obeying

hitting

good

bad

lying

taking turns

praying

Pray Ask God to help you make good choices and have good actions.

FRIDAY Ezekiel 36:27

God puts His Spirit inside of you to help you follow His laws.

Making good choices is hard sometimes. Write the first letter of each picture to see how God helps you to make good choices.

___ ___ ___ ___

Pray Ask God to help you want to follow His laws.

SATURDAY Ezekiel 37:3b

Only God can know what is going to happen in the future. He alone has the answers.

Draw a picture of what you would like to be when you grow up. Ask God if that is what His plan is for you.

Pray Thank God that He knows what is going to happen and that He takes care of you.

COMMENT CORNER

Parent or Leader, circle a comment and/or write your own.

You're special — You can do it — God loves you! — Nice job! — We're proud of you! — Keep it up — WOW!

DAYS COMPLETED

WEEK 36

SUNDAY Ezekiel 37:27

If you have asked God to be your God and Savior write your name on the heart. If you are not sure and would like to be, ask your parents or an adult at church.

God wants to be a part of your life. He wants to be your God and for you to be one of His people.

Pray Thank God that He loves you and wants to be in your life.

MONDAY Ezekiel 38:7

God wanted His people to be prepared to go into battle.

You are in a battle against sin every day. Check those things that will help you to win.

- Candy
- Games
- Prayer
- Good Friends
- Toys
- Bible

Pray Ask God to help you obey Him.

TUESDAY Ezekiel 38:16b

God shows Himself to others through you.

Circle the actions you can do to allow God's love to shine through you.

kindness

selfishness

love

friendliness

helpfulness

Pray Ask God to help your friends learn about Him through you.

WEDNESDAY Ezekiel 39:7

God wants you to know about Him.

Unscramble the words of ways you can know God better.

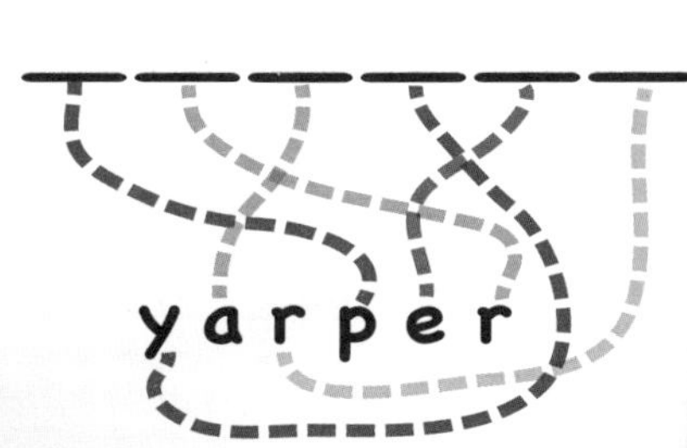

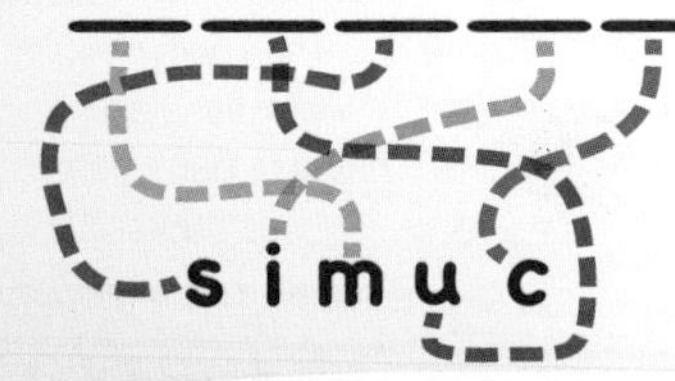

Pray

Ask God to help you know Him better every day.

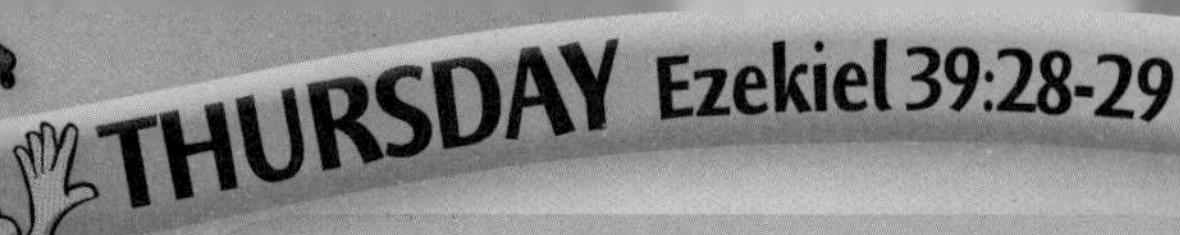

THURSDAY Ezekiel 39:28-29

Because God is holy He must punish sin, but His goal is to fix the relationship by forgiving your sins.

Use the code to unscramble this puzzle.

S2n = p4n2shm1nt

C3nf1ss23n = f3rg2v1n1ss

E=1 i=2 o=3 u=4

Pray

Thank God that He loves you enough to punish and forgive your sins.

FRIDAY Ezekiel 44:1

You show respect to God because He is holy.

Write every other letter in the circle.

Pray

Praise God for His holiness.

SATURDAY Ezekiel 47:12

Just like this river gives life and blessing, you can give blessings to others.

Circle the ways you can be a blessing to others.

Help wash dishes.

Make my bed.

Pick up my toys without being asked.

Watch TV.

Be nice to others

Pray

Ask God to help you be a blessing to someone today.

COMMENT CORNER

Parent or Leader, circle a comment and/or write your own.

You're special | You can do it | God loves you! | Nice job! | We're proud of you! | Keep it up | WOW!

DAYS COMPLETED

WEEK 37

"He Keeps Me Safe"

SUNDAY Revelation 6:10

Write the first letter of each picture to find the word that means being hurt because of what you believe.

Pray

Ask God to help people everywhere understand that God loves them.

MONDAY Revelation 7:9

God's people come from every country and can look very different from you.

Draw a line from the scrambled word to the unscrambled word to see some of the countries God's people come from.

nUdtei attesS	Mexico
crenFa	China
danglEn	United States
aniCh	England
ixeMoc	France

Pray

Praise God that He loves people of every color.

TUESDAY Revelation 8:8

The Bible mentions 7 angels playing instruments.

Write the letters to see what instrument they played.

_ _ _ _ _ _ _ _

Pray

Thank God for the sound of instruments. Tell Him what your favorite instrument is.

WEDNESDAY Revelation 9:15

God has plans for angels and God has plans for you.

Check all the things God has planned for your life.

- Do your best at school.
- Obey your parents.
- Make fun of kids who are different than you.
- Ask Jesus to be your Savior.
- Tell lies to your friends.
- Pray about everything.

Pray Ask God to help you follow His plan for your life.

THURSDAY Revelation 11:12

The Bible says one day you can go to Heaven away from your enemies.

Cross out three things that will NOT be in Heaven.

God
angels
enemies
streets of Gold
Jesus
hunger
sickness

Pray Thank God there will be no enemies in Heaven. Pray that your enemies will learn to love God.

FRIDAY Revelation 12:1

God prepares places of safety for you.

Write the words backwards to see 3 safe places God has provided for you.

emoh ______________

hcruhc ______________

loohcs ______________

Pray Tell God about one place you feel safe.

SATURDAY Revelation 13:7

Satan has no power of his own. His power is given to him from God.

God is more powerful than Satan. Underline the item that is more powerful in each pair.

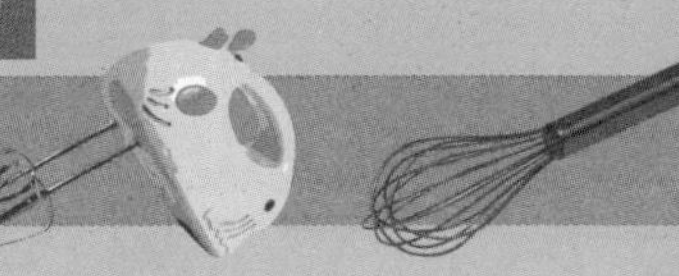

Pray Thank God that He is more powerful than Satan.

COMMENT CORNER

Parent or Leader, circle a comment and/or write your own.

You can do it · God loves you! · Nice job! · We're proud of you! · Keep it up · WOW!

DAYS COMPLETED

WEEK 38

"Surprise Party"

I heard on TV that Jesus is coming back before Christmas!

I think they need to read the book of Revelation.

Jesus said even He doesn't know the day of His return.

It will be a surprise party that is out of this world!

SUNDAY Revelation 14:1

Use the clues to discover the name of Jesus in today's verse.

It is an animal. Led by a shepherd. Usually white.

___ ___ ___ ___

Pray Tell Jesus you love Him.

Jesus has many different names in the Bible.

MONDAY Revelation 14:14

John saw Jesus sitting on a cloud. He was looking for everyone who had been faithful or unfaithful to Him.

You cannot hide from Jesus. He knows everything, and He knows your heart. You cannot act like you love Jesus when you really do not. Find the child and a heart hiding in the picture. Color the heart red to remind you that you cannot hide from Jesus.

Pray Ask God to help you be faithful to Him.

TUESDAY Revelation 15:3

Today's verse has another name for God.

Unscramble the letters to find the answer.

___ ___ ___ ___

n g i K

___ ___   ___ ___ ___

f o   h e t

___ ___ ___ ___

g A s e

Pray Praise God for being your King.

THURSDAY Revelation 16:15

Jesus is coming back to earth someday, but no one, not even Jesus, knows the day.

Draw a picture of what you might be doing when Jesus surprises us with His return.

Pray Ask God to help you make good choices until Jesus comes back again.

Pray Thank God that He sees everything.

FRIDAY Revelation 17: 8

Have you asked Jesus to be your Savior from sin? Is your name written in the book of life?

You don't have to worry about all the bad things that will happen in the future if you have asked Jesus to be your Savior. If you have asked Jesus to be your Savior, write your name in the book. If you need help asking Jesus to be your Savior, talk to your parents or an adult at church. If you know someone who needs Jesus, write their name on the other page and pray for them now.

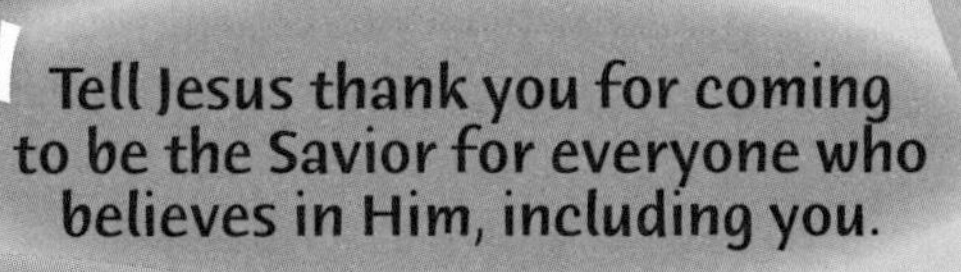

SATURDAY Revelation 17:17

God puts things into your heart to accomplish His purpose.

One of God's purposes is that the whole world would know about Him. Check off the things He might put in your heart to accomplish this week.

- ◇ Pray for your friends
- ◇ Play video games
- ◇ Give money to missions
- ◇ Invite your friends to church
- ◇ Watch TV

Pray Ask God to use you to help someone today.

COMMENT CORNER

Parent or Leader, circle a comment and/or write your own.

You're special · You can do it · God loves you! · Nice job! · We're proud of you! · Keep it up · WOW!

DAYS COMPLETED

WEEK 39

"No Time-Outs!"

Is that because the Bible says there is no sin in Heaven?

It is impossible to make bad choices in Heaven.

Even when I try to be good, I do something wrong.

Yeah! No sin means no punishments!

SUNDAY Revelation 19:9

The wedding feast is for those who have trusted Jesus as their Savior and have been faithful. It will be great feast. What do you think will be on the table to eat? Draw food on the plate that you hope will be there.

You have been invited to the wedding.

Pray Praise God for loving you so much.

MONDAY Revelation 19:16

In the end of time, the followers of Satan will be thrown into a lake of fire. Jesus will speak the truth to their armies, and they will die when they hear the truth.

Everything in God's Word is truth. Satan speaks only lies. Write the beginning sound of each picture on the line.

___ ___ ___ ___ ___

Pray Tell Jesus thank you for always speaking the truth.

TUESDAY Revelation 20:13

God is all-knowing. He sees everything that you do.

Cross out the actions that you would not want God to see you doing.

Hitting your sister

Doing your homework

Praying

Telling a lie

Playing soccer

Saying bad words

Pray Ask God to help you make good choices even when no one is looking.

WEDNESDAY Revelation 21:6

In the Book of Revelation God is called the Alpha and Omega.

Use the code to discover what these words mean.

__ __ __ __ __ __ __ __ __

and the __ __ __.

Pray

Thank God that He controls all things.

THURSDAY Revelation 21:27

There is no sin in Heaven. No sin means no punishment.

Can you imagine a day when you do nothing wrong? Find the letters in the picture and write them on the line to see where you can be perfect.

____

Pray Thank God for making a place where there is no sin.

FRIDAY Revelation 22:5

Are you ever afraid when the lights go out? It is never dark in Heaven. Jesus will light the whole place up.

Write the name of each light next to the picture.

head	desk	book	street

_ _ _ _ _ _ light

_ _ _ _ light

_ _ _ _ lamp

_ _ _ _ light

Pray Thank Jesus for being the light in Heaven.

SATURDAY Revelation 22:15

God says there will not be liars in Heaven. He feels very strongly about telling the truth.

Mike and Jenny saw Haley take one cookie from the cook jar. When asked by their mother if they saw anything they said the following. Place an L if they told a lie. Place a T if they told the truth.

_____ Jenny said she didn't see anything.

_____ Haley said she took 1 cookie.

_____ Mike said Haley took 3 cookies.

_____ Haley said Mike took 2 cookies.

_____ Jenny said Haley took one cookie.

_____ Mike said he took the cookie.

Pray

Ask God to help you tell the truth always.

COMMENT CORNER Parent or Leader, circle a comment and/ your own.

DAYS COMPLETED

You're special · You can do it · God loves you! · Nice job! · We're proud of you! · Keep it up · WOW!

WEEK 40

"Super Soap"

Chris, why do you keep washing your hands?

Soap can't take that feeling away.

I feel so dirty after yelling at my sister.

Only Jesus can help you with that.

SUNDAY Job 1:8

God said that Job was faithful and careful not to do anything evil. What does God say about you?

Circle the actions that God can say about you. Pray for God's help on the other ones.

Shares with siblings and friends

Obeys parents the first time

Tells the truth

Respects teachers

Uses kind words

Pray Ask God to help you always make good choices.

MONDAY Job 1:21

Job had bad things happen to him. He still chose to praise God.

Write the first letter of each picture to find the answer.

Job

God

even when bad things happened. That is how he could still praise God.

Tell God you will trust Him even when bad things happen.

TUESDAY Job 2:6

Satan is real, but God is stronger than him.

Check the activities you have to ask for permission before you do them.

- [ ] Cross the street to get your ball.
- [ ] Bike to your friend's house.
- [ ] Have a cookie before dinner.
- [ ] Scratch your head.
- [ ] Leave class to go to the restroom.

Pray Thank God that He is stronger than Satan.

WEDNESDAY Job 7:7

Job told God that he would never be happy again. It is good to tell God how you feel.

Feelings are emotions. Cross out the words that are not emotions.

Running

Angry Lonely

Excited

Talking

Happy

Pray

Thank God for caring about your feelings.

THURSDAY Job 9:4

God is wise and powerful. He is big enough to handle all your problems.

Follow the maze to help Josh with his problems.

Pray

Praise God that He is wise and strong.

FRIDAY Job 9:30

Job realized that soap could not take away his sin. He needed Jesus to forgive his sins, just like you do.

Mark each statement T (True) or F (False).

- ☐ Soap washes away dirt.
- ☐ I am a girl.
- ☐ Thursday comes after Friday.
- ☐ Jesus forgives my sin when I ask.
- ☐ I have sinned.
- ☐ Soap washes away my sin.

Pray

Tell Jesus about one bad choice you made today.

SATURDAY Job 13:10

God has the power to know your thoughts and help you change your thoughts.

Circle every third letter. Write the letters on the blank to see one way to change your thoughts.

DHBWRELKIDDNBNG
CVTMCHTYAALNOIKFFFWEUPOL

_____ _____ _____ _____ _____

_____ _____ _____ _____ _____ _____ _____ _____

Pray

Thank God for His power to help you change your thoughts.

COMMENT CORNER

Parent or Leader, circle a comment and/or write your own.

You're special You can do it God loves you! Nice job! We're proud of you! Keep it up WOW!

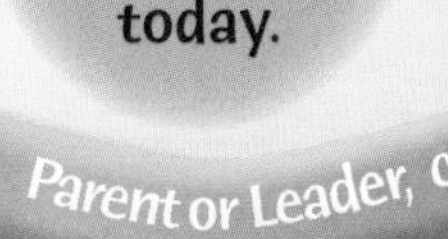

DAYS COMPLETED

WEEK 41

"Read My Mind"

You must have read my mind. That is what I was thinking.

Today is a perfect day for a banana split.

Can Katie really read minds?

No, only God knows what we are thinking.

SUNDAY Job 14:5

Draw a line to the correct answer. Daniel is the oldest. Emmanuel is the youngest. Emma is older than Kayla.

Emma	10
Daniel	3
Kayla	7
Emmanuel	5

You do not have to be afraid of dying. God knew before you were born how long you would live and when you would die. He is in control.

Pray Thank God that He knows when you were born and when you will die.

MONDAY Job 17:15

When Job got very, very sad he told God how he felt.

There are many ways to express your emotions to God. Check each way you would express your emotions.

- Pray in your bed
- Talk to an adult
- Draw a picture about it
- Pray when you are swinging
- Sing God a song

Pray Thank God that He cares when you are very sad.

TUESDAY Job 19:25

Job believed that Jesus would take care of him. Like Job, you are praying to a God that is alive and has power.

Unscramble the letters and write them on the line.

t s e u r d

Job had pain and was sad, but he ________ God.

Pray Ask Jesus to help you remember that He is alive and will take care of you.

WEDNESDAY Job 23:11

Job said that his feet closely followed Jesus. Can you say that you are living like Jesus?

Cross out the footprints that are NOT like Jesus.

Thankful

Honest

Helpful

Disrespect

Obey

Lie

Pray

Ask God to help you act like Jesus.

THURSDAY Job 38:12

God asked Job, "Have you ever told the new day to come?" The ability and smarts that you have will never compare to what God has.

Draw a line through the action that you DO NOT have the ability to do.

Tie my shoes

Make it snow

Smile

Hug my mom

Make my bed

Pray

Praise God that He has the power to change nighttime to daytime.

FRIDAY Job 40:5

Job admitted that he was wrong. Do you admit it when you are wrong?

Write the first letter of each picture to see another word for admit.

___ ___ ___ ___ ___ ___ ___

Pray

Thank God that He gives you the power to admit when you are wrong.

SATURDAY Job 42:7

God takes it very seriously when you don't tell the truth about Him to your friends.

Draw a line through the statements about God that are NOT true.

God loves everyone.

There are lots of gods.

Everyone is going to Heaven.

Jesus came back to life.

God doesn't mind little lies.

Pray

Ask God to help you always tell the truth.

COMMENT CORNER

Parent or Leader, circle a comment and/or write your own.

You're special | You can do it | God loves you! | Nice job! | We're proud of you! | Keep it up | WOW!

DAYS COMPLETED

WEEK 42

"Pleasing Lives"

In the book of 1 Peter, God tells us things we can do to please Him.

Yeah, like trusting Him even during hard times.

We learn, too, that we should love and respect people.

And don't forget about getting rid of the bad things in our lives.

SUNDAY 1 Peter 1:7

Find the three things in the word search that God receives when you trust Him.

Y	I	K	G	O	I
P	R	A	I	S	E
J	H	O	N	O	R
G	P	Q	K	O	I
M	G	L	O	R	Y

Trust God even during the hard times. When you do this, you bring glory, praise, and honor to God.

Pray Ask God to help you trust Him no matter what.

MONDAY 1 Peter 1:15-16

Jesus came to earth as a holy (perfect) person. Jesus never sinned. You need to try to be just like Jesus. You need to obey in everything.

What do you need to practice all the time? Start at the arrow and write every other letter on the line. Then pray and ask God to help you be obedient.

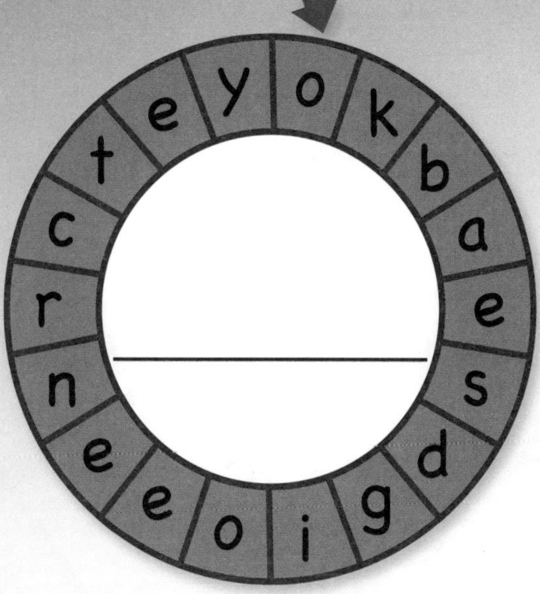

Pray Ask Jesus to help you be like Him today.

TUESDAY 1 Peter 1:25

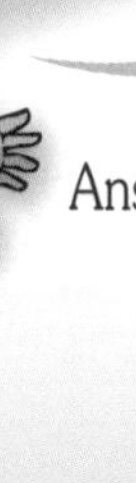

The Bible is sometimes called the "Word of the Lord." You can know for sure that the Bible is true today. You can know the Bible will be true forever.

Answer the questions. Then complete the crossword puzzle.

The "Word of the Lord" is the B____.[1]

The Bible is t___[2] today and f______.[3]

Pray Thank God for the Bible that is true forever.

WEDNESDAY 1 Peter 2:1

God wants you to get rid of the bad things in your heart. When you get rid of the bad things, replace them with good things.

Draw a line to match the opposites. Choose one good thing that you can do. Pray and ask God to help you do that good thing today.

lying	telling the truth
disobeying	loving
stealing	sharing
hating	obeying

Pray Ask God to help you tell the truth.

THURSDAY 1 Peter 2:17

God wants you to love other people. God wants you to respect the people who are in charge of you.

Put a checkmark by the things you should do.

___ Tell someone you love them.

___ Listen to your teacher.

___ Say hurtful things.

___ Obey your parents.

___ Do whatever you want to do.

Pray Thank God for all the people who love you.

FRIDAY 1 Peter 2:24

Jesus lived a perfect life. It was because of your sin that He died on the cross.

Trace the words on the cross. If you have asked Jesus to be your Savior, thank Him for dying for your sin. If you have never asked Jesus to be your Savior, talk to your parent or an adult at church.

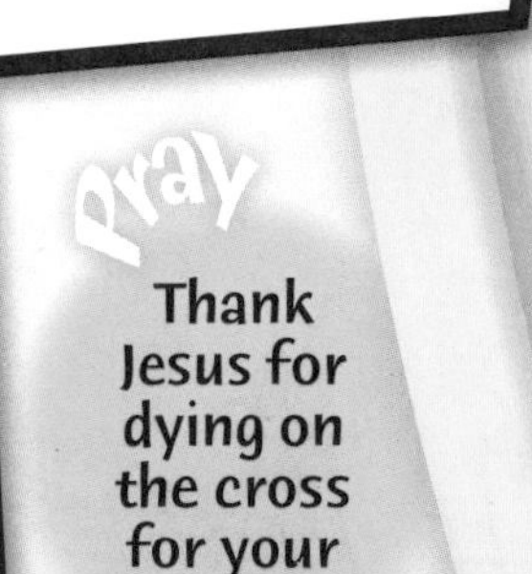

My Sin

Pray Thank Jesus for dying on the cross for your sin.

SATURDAY 1 Peter 3:4b

Guess what God thinks is great? God thinks it's great when you are gentle and kind to others.

How should you act toward others? Draw a line from 1 to 6, then draw a line from A to B. Next draw a line from 1 to 4. Lastly, draw a line from a to f.

1 • 4 • A • 2 • 5 • 3 • 2 • 6 • B • 1 • 4 • a • f • e • d • c • b • 3

Pray Ask God to help you be kind today.

COMMENT CORNER Parent or Leader, circle a comment and/or write your own.

You're special · You can do it · God loves you! · Nice job! · We're proud of you! · Keep it up · WOW!

DAYS COMPLETED

WEEK 43

"Keep On"

At times it's not easy being a Christian. Sometimes even your friends might make fun of you for doing what is right.

Then what should you do?

The book of 1 Peter says keep on doing what is right.

Yeah, and trust God. He cares for you.

SUNDAY 1 Peter 3:11

You're playing with friends and someone gets upset. Your friends start to argue. Use a mirror to read the message of what you should do. Write the answer on the line.

Look for Peace

Today's Bible verse tells you to look for peace. You should try to make things right.

____

Pray Ask God to help you look for peace.

MONDAY 1 Peter 3:18

Jesus died for the bad things you have done. Jesus died to bring you to God.

Read the sentences. If the sentence is true give the thumbs up sign. If the sentence is false give the thumbs down sign.

Jesus died for the bad thing you have done.

Jesus died for the bad things He had done.

Jesus died to bring you to God.

Pray Thank Jesus for dying on the cross for your sin.

TUESDAY 1 Peter 4:2

You should always be ready to do the things God wants you to do.

You need to follow God's path and not your own path. Take the children through the maze. When you are finished, ask God to help you do the things He wants you to do.

Pray Ask God to help you follow His ways every day.

WEDNESDAY 1 Peter 4:8

Most important of all you should show love to other people. When you show love, God will help you to forgive people.

Find the hidden letters in the picture. Put the letters in order to find out what you should show others.

Pray

Ask God to help you show love to others.

THURSDAY 1 Peter 4:19

It's not always easy to do the things God wants you to do. Sometimes your friends might make fun of you. When that happens, just keep doing what is right. Trust God and keep doing good things.

Draw a picture of one good thing you can do today.

Pray

Ask God to help you do what is right.

FRIDAY 1 Peter 5:7

Whenever you are worried or upset, ask Jesus to take care of it. Jesus cares about what happens to you.

Fill in the words to the song "Jesus Loves Me." Then sing the song with a friend or parent.

Yes, Jesus ________ me.

Yes, Jesus loves _____.

Yes, ________ loves me.

The _________ tells

_____ so.

Pray

Thank Jesus that He loves and cares for you.

SATURDAY 1 Peter 5:8

You need to be very careful. Watch out! The devil will do anything to make you sin.

Write the first letter of each picture to see your enemy's name.

___ ___ ___   ___ ___ ___ ___ ___

Pray

Ask God to help you follow Him and not the devil's tricks.

COMMENT CORNER

Parent or Leader, circle a comment and/or write your own.

You're special · You can do it · God loves you! · Nice job! · We're proud of you! · Keep it up · WOW!

DAYS COMPLETED

WEEK 44

"A Wise King for Israel"

SUNDAY 1 Kings 1:29-30

Find the 3 hidden letters in the palace and write them on the line.

God helped King David when he was in trouble. David knew he had to decide who would be the king after he died. He said he would keep his promise to his wife Bathsheba. Their son, Solomon, would be the next king.

Pray Ask God to help you when you are having troubles.

____

MONDAY 1 Kings 2:3-4

King David reminded Solomon that, in order to be a good king, he needed to follow God's laws carefully. If Solomon obeyed God, he would be a great king.

What should you obey to be successful?
Find the message by filling in the letter that goes with the number. (For example: 1 = A, 2 = B, 3 = C)

A	D	G	I	L	O	S	U	V	W
21	12	13	25	6	26	22	2	24	4

__ __ __ ' __ __ __ __ __
13 26 12 22 6 21 4 22

Pray Tell God thank you for His Word, the Bible, written to you.

TUESDAY 1 Kings 3:9

King Solomon could have asked for anything. He asked God for wisdom and understanding so he could be a good and kind king. God was pleased with King Solomon's request.

God wants you to be good and kind. Cross out the WRONG ending to the sentence, and circle the RIGHT ending.

When your friend hits you...	you hit him back. you turn and walk away.
If your sister doesn't have a treat...	you share your snack. you say "Too bad!"
If your brother falls down...	you run the other way. you stop and help him.

Pray Ask God to help you be good and kind.

WEDNESDAY 1 Kings 3:28

All the people in Israel knew that King Solomon's wisdom came from God. The people respected the king's judgment.

Finish the crossword puzzle.

ACROSS

1. The people ________ King Solomon's judgment.

DOWN

2. God gave King Solomon ________.

3. King Solomon's wisdom came from ____.

Pray

Ask God to help you make right choices.

THURSDAY 1 Kings 4:34

King Solomon was the wisest man in the world. God gave him his wisdom and power. People would come from other countries to hear the king speak.

Follow the maze to get the people to King Solomon.

Pray

Ask God to help you listen to wise people.

FRIDAY 1 Kings 6:12-13

God told King Solomon that he would be blessed for obeying God and building the temple. The temple would be a special place for the people of Israel to worship God.

God's people first worshipped in the tabernacle, then the temple, and now the church. Number the places of worship in the order they should go. Draw a circle around where you worship God.

Pray

Tell God thank you for your church.

SATURDAY 1 Kings 11:9-10

King Solomon did not continue to follow the one and only God. He began to worship pretend gods. This made God angry. Even though King Solomon was wise, he made the wrong choice.

You can find wisdom to help you make good choices when you read your Bible. Draw lines from the words in the space to God's Word or Satan and Sin.

Good Choices

God's Word

Idol Worship

Obedience

Satan and Sin

Lying

Peace

Pray

Ask God to forgive you for something you have done wrong.

COMMENT CORNER

Parent or Leader, circle a comment and/or write your own.

You're special · You can do it · God loves you! · Nice job! · We're proud of you! · Keep it up · WOW!

DAYS COMPLETED

WEEK 45

"Bad Kings - Bad Choices"

SUNDAY 1 Kings 12:8

The new king, Rehoboam, wanted everyone to know that he was in charge. Instead of listening to the older men who were wise, he listened to his friends. This made the people angry.

Use a red crayon to circle the group the king listened to. With a blue crayon, circle the group you should listen to.

Pray

Ask God to help you listen to your parents.

MONDAY 1 Kings 12:23-24

God didn't want Rehoboam to fight against his own people. God doesn't want you to fight with others, either. You should get along with your brothers, sisters, and friends.

What instruction did God give Israel about what they should do instead of fighting with each other?

★ = O
▲ = M
■ = H
● = G
X = E

___ ___   ___ ___ ___ ___
● ★   ■ ★ ▲ X

Pray

Ask God to help you to be kind to others.

TUESDAY 1 Kings 13:6

The king asked the man of God to pray for him to be healed. God answered his prayer by healing the king's hand. God does listen when you pray. Keep talking to Him.

Write two things you are praying for, and pray for them right now.

Pray

Thank God for hearing and answering your prayers.

WEDNESDAY 1 Kings 13:18-19

The man of God was supposed to go straight home. Another man lied to him and tricked him into disobeying God. God said he would be punished for disobeying Him and listening to lies.

Cross out all the A's and O's to find the message. Write it on the line.

O L O A O O O W i l l O O
A O y i O g A O A O O
A n O O A O O
A b e O A u n O A d
b O A p O i s h e O
O A O A i O A

Pray Ask God to help you tell the truth.

THURSDAY 1 Kings 17:5-6

God provided food and water for Elijah even though there was no rain. God used birds and a small brook to take care of Elijah.

God takes care of you, too. Color the picture showing where Elijah stayed during the famine.

Black = Blue = Green = Red =

Pray Tell God thank you for the food He gives you.

FRIDAY 1 Kings 17:15-16

Elijah went to a woman during the time of famine and asked her to make him food. She did as he asked. God gave the widow and her son all the food they needed because she helped Elijah. You should help others, too!

Circle the pictures you could use to make a snack or a meal for someone.

Pray Pray for an older person who needs help.

SATURDAY 1 Kings 18:1-2

God was getting ready to send rain after three years of famine. He told Elijah to go to Ahab, the evil king, and tell him it would rain soon. God is in control of all nature.

Color the shapes with dots blue to see what was on its way.

Pray Thank God for making the sunshine and the rain.

COMMENT CORNER

Parent or Leader, circle a comment and/or write your own.

You're special · You can do it · God loves you! · Nice job! · We're proud of you! · Keep it up · WOW!

DAYS COMPLETED

WEEK 46

"Fire From Heaven"

The people worshipped idols.

We should worship only God.

Yeah! He's the only true God.

SUNDAY 1 Kings 18:18

There is only one God. You need to worship Him. Circle the hidden 1's in the picture.

The people were not worshiping God. They were bowing down to idols instead. Elijah decided to show them Who the only true God really was.

Pray

Praise God for being the one true God.

MONDAY 1 Kings 18:38-39

Elijah built an altar to God. He put a bull on it and covered it with water. Elijah prayed to God. God sent fire from Heaven to burn up the sacrifice, stones, and water. When the people saw this, they believed in God.

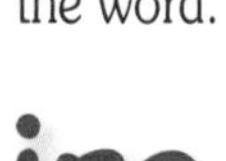

Draw flaming fire on the altar that was burned up by God. Write a letter from the box to finish the word.

__ire

Pray

Tell God thank you for His great power.

TUESDAY 1 Kings 18:46

Elijah told King Ahab to go home because it was going to rain. Ahab got into his chariot and hurried home. Elijah ran in the power of the Lord and got to Jezreel before King Ahab did.

God is very powerful. Draw 2 lines to take King Ahab and Elijah back to Jezreel.

Pray

Ask God for something you or your family needs.

WEDNESDAY 1 Kings 19:11-12

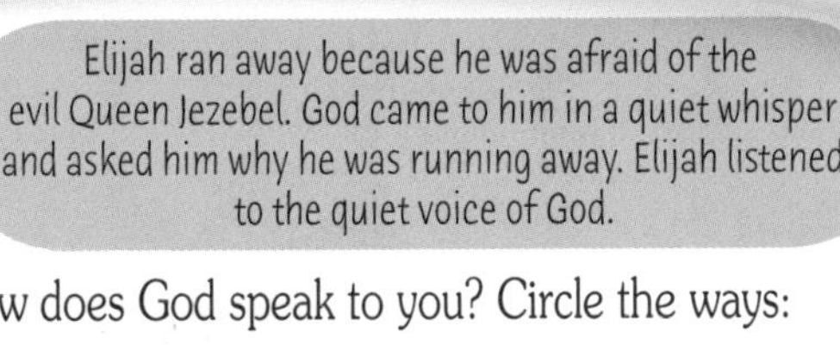

Elijah ran away because he was afraid of the evil Queen Jezebel. God came to him in a quiet whisper and asked him why he was running away. Elijah listened to the quiet voice of God.

How does God speak to you? Circle the ways:

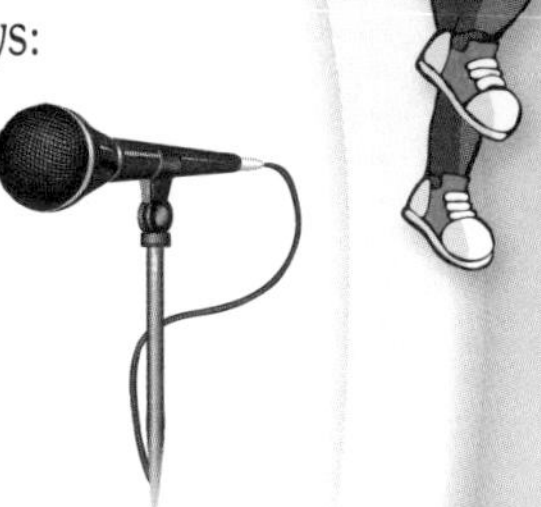

Pray
Thank God for the Bible.

THURSDAY 1 Kings 21:2-4

King Ahab wanted to buy Naboth's vineyard and make it into a vegetable garden. Naboth would not sell it to him. The king got mad. He pouted and complained and would not eat.

How do you act when you don't get your way? Check "yes" or "no" to answer the questions.

YES	NO	
☐	☐	You should always get what you want.
☐	☐	When you don't get what you want, you should get angry and pout.
☐	☐	You should be happy even if you don't get your way.

Pray
Ask God to help you be thankful.

FRIDAY 1 Kings 21:25-29

Ahab was a wicked king. He did evil in God's sight. Elijah told King Ahab that he and all his family would be punished. Ahab realized he was wrong and called out to God. God still had to punish Ahab's family for his sin.

Put the first letter of each picture in the box to see what God will do when you ask Him to.

Pray
Ask God to forgive you for something you have done wrong.

SATURDAY 1 Kings 22:30

King Ahab tried to trick the other army. He knew they were after him. Even then, God was in control.

God will take care of you. Hold the page in front of a mirror to read the secret message.

God is in control.

Pray
Thank Jesus for dying on the cross for you.

COMMENT CORNER Parent or Leader, circle a comment and/or write your own.

You're special · You can do it · God loves you! · Nice job! · We're proud of you! · Keep it up · WOW!

DAYS COMPLETED

WEEK 47
"Who's Your Hero?"
A hero is someone you want to be like.
I want to be like a movie star.
My hero is the greatest baseball player ever.
I want Jesus to be my hero. I want to be just like Him.
SUNDAY 2 Kings 1:3
Fill in the vowels to sing the song.
a e i o u y
The B-_- b-l_,
yes that's the book for me.
I'll r_ _d and pr_ _
and then _b_ _
The B-_- b-l_. B_bl_!
You are only to look to the God of the Bible for answers. No one with magical powers knows as much as your God does.
Pray
Ask God to help you understand His Word, the Bible.
MONDAY 2 Kings 2:9
Elisha's hero was the man of God, Elijah. Elisha wanted to be just like Elijah. Who do you want to be like?
List three people who love God like you want to love God.
My Heroes
1. ______
2. ______
3. ______
Pray
Tell God you want to show your friends how to love Him.
TUESDAY 2 Kings 2: 14
Elisha acted just like his friend Elijah. Since his friend made good choices this was a good thing. Whom do you act like?
You tend to act like your friends, which is why you need to choose your friends carefully. Find 6 words that show good friend qualities.
KIND
PEACEFUL
SHARING
LOVING
RESPECTFUL
PATIENT
U X H S H A R I N G B T
U M R E S P E C T F U L
Z M C D G S L O V I N G
E I L Q V F S T R O K J
E U N X D K I N D X W B
P A T I E N T A V L C L
S K W W P E A C E F U L
Pray
Ask God to help you choose friends who make good choices.

WEDNESDAY 2 Kings 4:2

God wants you to use what you have now to serve Him. He doesn't want you to wait till you grow up and have lots of money.

Think about things you have in your house that you can use to bless others. Circle 3 things you could use today.

cookies

outgrown clothes

hugs

2 of the same toy

smiles

books too young for you

too many stuffed animals

time to listen

Pray

Ask God to show you what you could share today.

THURSDAY 2 Kings 4:22

When this lady had a problem she didn't fuss, she went right to God to get help.

When you have a problem it is good to talk to someone about it. Unscramble the words to see whom you can talk to. Circle the one you should talk to first.

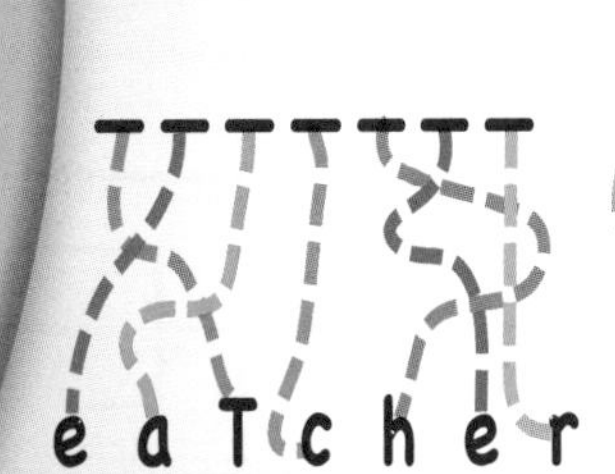

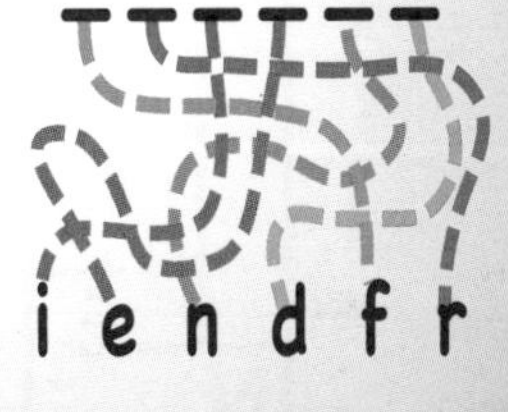

Tell God that you will tell Him your problem first.

FRIDAY 2 Kings 4:38

Elisha didn't have very much, but what he had he shared.

Blake had 10 pieces of candy. He gave 2 to his dad and 1 to his mom. His brother wanted 3 pieces. How many did Blake have left?

10

– ______

– ______

– ______

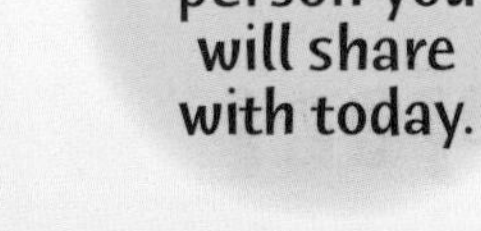

Tell God the name of one person you will share with today.

SATURDAY 2 Kings 5:10

Sometimes God's way of doing things just doesn't make sense to you. Naaman obeyed even though he didn't understand.

Put a check beside the things you have to do that don't make sense. Will you be like Naaman and obey even if you don't understand?

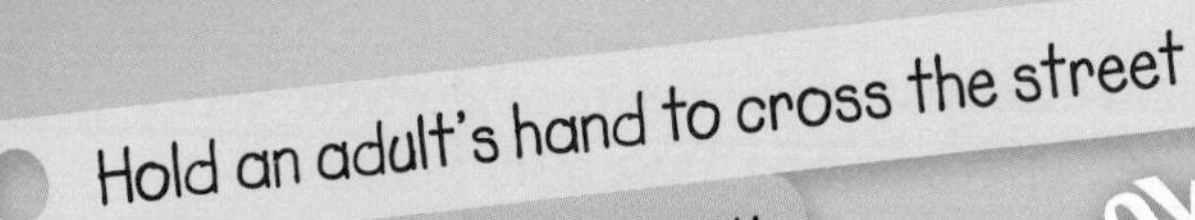

- Hold an adult's hand to cross the street
- Always wear a seat belt
- Eat dinner before dessert
- Wash your hands before you eat
- Wear your bike helmet
- Do your homework before watching TV

Pray

Ask God to help you obey even when you don't understand.

COMMENT CORNER

Parent or Leader, circle a comment and/or write your own.

You're special · You can do it · God loves you! · Nice job! · We're proud of you! · Keep it up · WOW!

DAYS COMPLETED

WEEK 48

"Got Your Back"

That ball almost hit me!

Good thing Joey was watching out for you and made you duck.

That would have really hurt.

No problem. I've got your back.

SUNDAY 2 Kings 5:22

Find out what Gehazi's punishment was. Follow the maze and pick up letters to fill in the blanks.

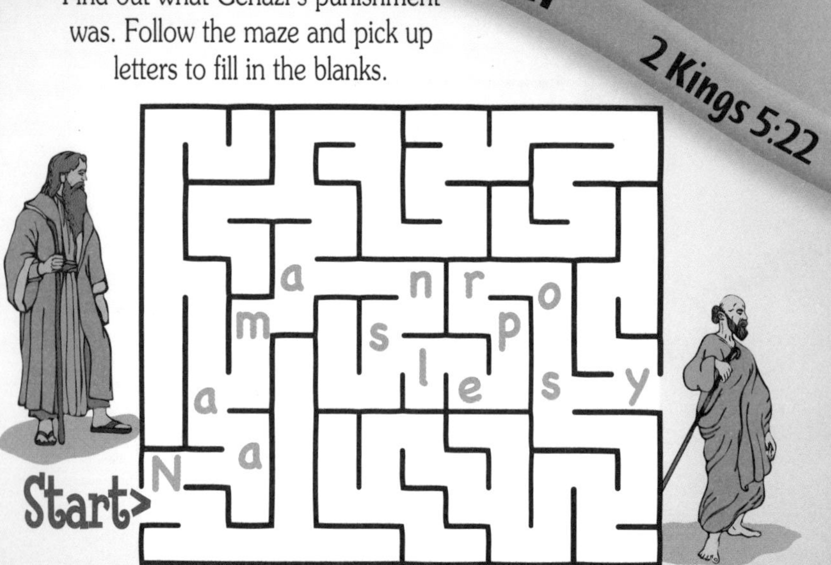

He received

_ _ _ _ _ _ ' _   _ _ _ _ _ _ _ _.

Gehazi told Naaman a lie. God punished Gehazi for that sin.

Pray Ask God to help you make good choices.

MONDAY 2 Kings 6:5

The man was very upset when his borrowed tool was lost. He was concerned because it did not belong to him.

Like this man you should be extra careful when you are borrowing something. Draw a line from the person to the item you might borrow from them.

teacher	soccer ball
grandpa	rake
friend	pencil
mother	tape
neighbor	tape measure

Pray Tell God you will be careful when you borrow something.

TUESDAY 2 Kings 6:23

Because the king was kind to his enemies they stopped going to war against him. What do you think would happen if you were kind to the classmate who is mean to you?

Kindness is the opposite of meanness. Draw a line to connect the opposites.

smile	keep
share	frown
invite	mean
kind	reject

Pray Tell God the name of one person you will try to be kind to today.

WEDNESDAY 2 Kings 6:32

Elisha's friends helped to protect him. How do you protect your friends?

Put an H in front of each statement that shows how to help a friend.

__Encourage him to cheat on a test to get a better grade

__Encourage her to tell her mom the truth even if she gets punished

__Warn him of the danger of crossing the street by himself

__Offer to loan her your extra bike helmet

__Ask him to help you start a fire in your backyard

Pray Ask God to help you protect your friends.

THURSDAY 2 Kings 7:9

The men knew they had to tell everyone the good news that they had found food.

What good news do you have to share? Write 3 things about Jesus that are good news to tell.

Pray Tell God the name of one person you will tell the Good News to today.

FRIDAY 2 Kings 7:18

Elisha told the people what was going to happen the next day. There was food in the land to sell, and it sold for the price he said. Elisha had spoken the truth.

God had told Elisha what to speak. Use the key to fill in the blanks.

A	D	E	G	H	K	L	O
1	2	3	4	5	6	7	8

P	R	S	T	U	W	Y
9	10	11	12	13	14	15

__ __ __   __ __ __ __ __ __
4 8 2   1 7 14 1 15 11

__ __ __ __ __ __
11 9 3 1 6 11

__ __ __ __ __
12 10 13 12 5

Thank God that He will do everything He says He will do. **Pray**

SATURDAY 2 Kings 9:6

Elisha gave Jehu a hard job to do. Jehu got right up and did as he was told. How fast do you respond to jobs you are given to do?

Put a Q in front of jobs you are quick to do and an S in front of jobs you are slow to do.

__homework

__making your bed

__brushing your teeth before bed

__soccer drills

__setting the table

__practicing your flash cards

__eating your breakfast

Pray Ask God to help you be quick to obey like Jehu.

COMMENT CORNER Parent or Leader, circle a comment and/or write your own.

You're special · You can do it · God loves you! · Nice job! · We're proud of you! · Keep it up · WOW!

DAYS COMPLETED

WEEK 49
"Made My Day"
Candice has been sick all week.
Hey, why don't we make her a get well card?
She even missed the class party.
I bet that will make her day.
SUNDAY 2 Kings 13:14
Circle the statement that tells how to live with God forever.
Make good choices
Go to church
Ask Jesus to be your Savior
Memorize Bible verses
Obey your parents
Feed the dog
Give money to poor people
Everyone dies. If you accept Jesus as your Savior you will go to live with Him someday. If you don't accept Jesus you will be separated from Him forever.
Pray
Thank God that He made a way for you to go to Heaven.
MONDAY 2 Kings 17:9
The Israelites thought they were hiding their bad choices. But God sees everything. Nothing is hidden from Him.
Find and circle the 5 animals hidden in the picture.
Pray
Ask God to forgive you for the bad choices you try to hide.
TUESDAY 2 Kings 17:26
Some of your friends may not know how to make good choices because they do not know about God.
How can you tell your friends about God? Follow the lines and write the letters.
t i l v m
u
to
r
c
h
n
e
Pray
Tell God the name of one of your friends that you will invite to church.

WEDNESDAY 2 Kings 19:6

When someone tells you something you need to decide if it is true. Just because they told you something doesn't make it true.

God can give you wisdom to know if something is true or not. Mark the following T for True or F for False.

- __The earth is flat.
- __All trees lose their leaves.
- __All babies are boys.
- __Caterpillars turn into butterflies.
- __When baby teeth fall out new teeth grow in.

Pray Thank God for giving you wisdom.

THURSDAY 2 Kings 19:5

How special to know that when you cry God sees your tears and hears your prayers.

Write God a thank you note.

Thank you God for seeing me when I cried about________________________.

You listened to me when I talked to you about________________________.

You are never too busy for me.

Pray Thank God that He is never too busy to listen to you.

FRIDAY 2 Kings 20:12

The king of Babylon sent Hezekiah letters and a gift because he knew that Hezekiah was sick.

Do you know someone who is sick? Circle what you could do to let them know that you care.

Call them

Send a card in the mail

Bake them cookies

Draw them a picture

Pray for them

Pray Tell God the name of someone who is sick.

SATURDAY 2 Kings 22:3

The king wanted the people to hear God's Word and promise to obey it.

Write every other letter on the blanks.

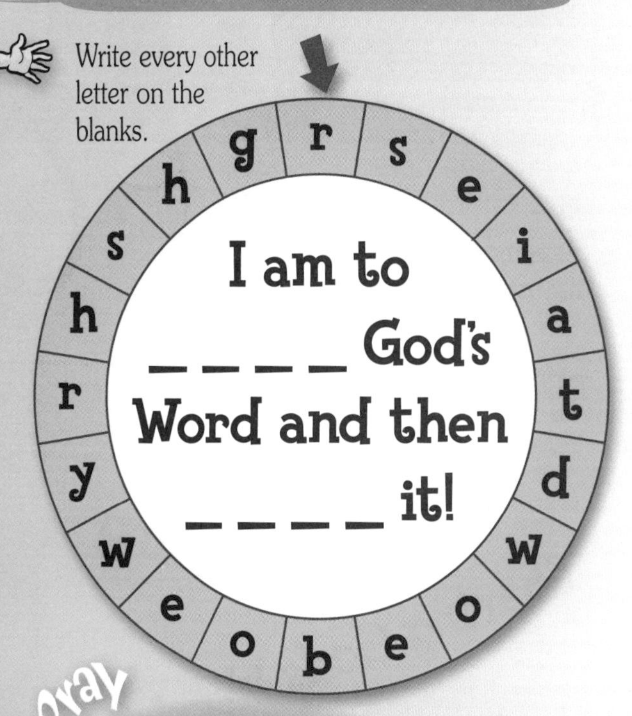

Pray Ask God to help you obey Him.

COMMENT CORNER

Parent or Leader, circle a comment and/or write your own.

You're special · You can do it · God loves you! · Nice job! · We're proud of you! · Keep it up · WOW!

DAYS COMPLETED

WEEK 50

"Our Inheritance"

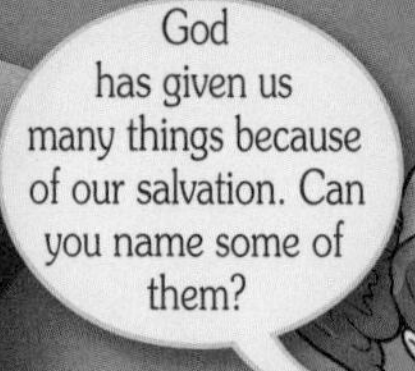

SUNDAY Ephesians 1:5

God has chosen you and adopted you as His child. God wants you to be excited that you are a part of His family.

Add your picture to the picture of God's family if you have asked Jesus to be your Savior. Talk to your parents or an adult at church if you are not sure.

Pray

Thank God for His great love for you.

MONDAY Ephesians 1:12

As a Christian you should live right for God and do things that bring praise to Him.

Circle the words below that bring praise to God.

Hitting
Helping Others
Obeying
Cheating
Sharing God's Word
Saying Bad Words

Pray

Ask God to help you do things that make Him happy.

TUESDAY Ephesians 1:19

You have power to do great things for God because He works in you and through you.

Hold your Quiet Time Diary up to a mirror. What does God give you? Write the word on the line.

power

____

Pray

Thank God for giving you strength to do good things when you ask Him.

WEDNESDAY Ephesians 2:4-5

God loves you so much that He wanted to save you from your sin even before you knew about Him.

Count by twos from 2 to 24 to connect the dots. Trace the letters written on the cross to see what God says to you.

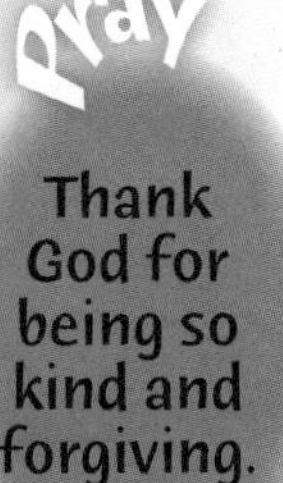

2 4 6 8 10 12 14 16 18 20 22 24

Pray

Thank God for being so kind and forgiving.

THURSDAY Ephesians 2:8-9

The only way you can be saved from your sin is by believing that Jesus died on the cross to take your punishment. You cannot do anything on your own to be saved.

Jesus gave you the free gift of salvation. Use the color code to color the picture.

1=Yellow
2= Blue
3= Red

Pray

Thank God for His free gift of salvation.

FRIDAY Ephesians 2:18

You can pray to God without having to have someone else pray for you. You can pray to God any time you want.

When is each child praying? Write the time.

____:______

____:______

____:______

Pray

Tell God thank you for always listening when you pray.

SATURDAY Ephesians 2:19

When you ask Jesus to save you from your sin, you are part of God's family and no longer a stranger to God.

Follow the path that a child of God takes once he is saved and becomes part of God's family.

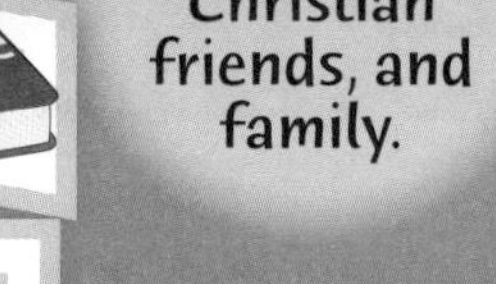

Pray

Ask God to bless your church, your Christian friends, and family.

COMMENT CORNER

Parent or Leader, circle a comment and/or write your own.

You're special · You can do it · God loves you! · Nice job! · We're proud of you! · Keep it up · WOW!

DAYS COMPLETED

"Step by Step"

God called Paul to be a minister for Him. He has a plan for us as well.

Because Christ lives in me I have God's power to follow His plan for me.

I can ask God whenever I need help because He's always there for me.

SUNDAY Ephesians 3:7

Solve the riddles to draw in the missing parts.

1) You use your ____________ to tell others about God.

2) Others use their ____________ to hear you.

God gave Paul the power to be a minister for Him. You, too, can be a minister for God.

Pray

Ask God to help you be brave and tell others about Him.

MONDAY Ephesians 3:12

You can talk to God whenever you want to, and you don't have to be scared that you are bothering Him.

Hold up the message to a mirror to find out what you need to have when you pray. Write the message on the line.

Boldness
Confidence

____

____

Pray

Thank God for listening when you pray.

TUESDAY Ephesians 3:20

God is so powerful. He can do more than you ask Him to do. He can do more than you can imagine. And He can do it in you and for you.

Color the letters with dots to see what God gives to you that is so great you cannot even imagine.

Pray

Praise God for His power.

WEDNESDAY Ephesians 4:3

God wants you to keep the peace with those you live with—that means getting along with them, no matter what.

These children are at peace with each other. Under each picture, write a word from the oval.

dig jump slide

Pray

Ask God to help you not to fight, but to get along with others.

THURSDAY Ephesians 4:15

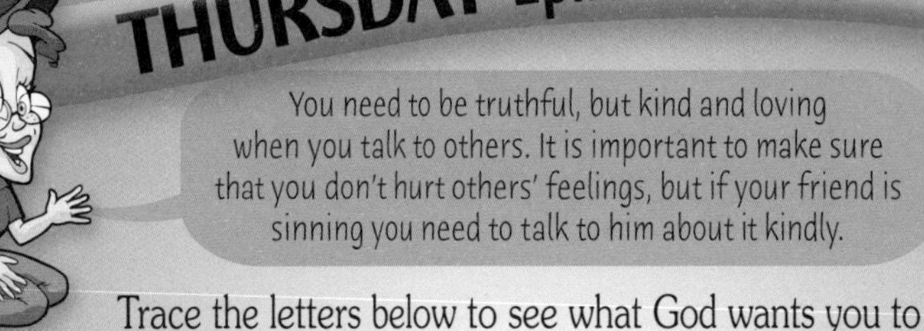

You need to be truthful, but kind and loving when you talk to others. It is important to make sure that you don't hurt others' feelings, but if your friend is sinning you need to talk to him about it kindly.

Trace the letters below to see what God wants you to speak from your mouth.

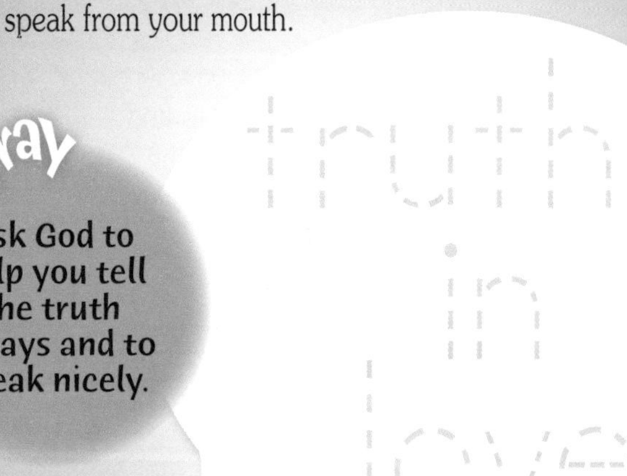

Pray

Ask God to help you tell the truth always and to speak nicely.

FRIDAY Ephesians 4:24

When you ask Jesus to be your Savior, you need to live for God and not live for yourself as you did before.

Draw a line through the maze to the correct answer.

I need to obey God's Word.

I can do anything I want to do.

Pray

Ask God to help you be strong and do only what He wants you to do.

SATURDAY Ephesians 4:32

You need to be kind all the time and be willing to forgive others when they hurt you.

Has someone done something wrong to you? Write the first name of someone who has wronged or hurt you. Now, forgive them for doing this to you even if they did not ask for your forgiveness.

Pray

Ask God to help you be kind and forgive someone who has hurt you.

COMMENT CORNER

Parent or Leader, circle a comment and/or write your own.

You're special · You can do it · God loves you! · Nice job! · We're proud of you! · Keep it up · WOW!

DAYS COMPLETED

WEEK 52
"Obedience is the Very Best Way"
God wants us to be obedient to those He has put in charge of us. Name some of those people.
Our teachers.
Our parents.
SUNDAY Ephesians 5:1
Your footsteps should follow God's. Write every other letter in the circle to find out Whom you should follow. Write the letters in the blanks as you follow the path.
I a f t o p l t l n o u w a G r o p d t
_ should
_ _ _ _ _ _ _
_ _ _.
You should want to be just like God, Who is your Heavenly Father. You should want to follow His footsteps.
Pray
Ask God to help you be like Him in the things you do and the things you say.
MONDAY Ephesians 5:10
God wants you to find out what pleases Him so you will behave as His child. As you read your Bible, you will discover things that you ought to do to please God.
Cross out the things that do not please God. Put a check mark beside the things that do please God. Ask God to help you please Him with your life.
obey my parents
lie
read my Bible
tell the truth
hit my friend
Pray
Ask God to help you learn what pleases Him.
TUESDAY Ephesians 5:20
You need to give God thanks for everything.
Write the beginning letter sound of each picture.
Pray
Tell God thank you for 3 things He has given you.

WEDNESDAY Ephesians 5:33

God wants husbands and wives to love and respect each other. They need to love each other more than they love themselves.

Look at each row. Color the heart to complete the pattern.

Pray

Pray for your dad and mom today.

THURSDAY Ephesians 6:1

God's Word, the Bible, says you need to obey your parents. You always need to obey them the first time, even if it isn't what you want to do. This pleases God.

Obeying

I need to obey my parents.
I'll tell you why:
Because

_____________ _____________

tells me to.

Pray Ask God to help you obey your parents all the time.

FRIDAY Ephesians 6:13

By reading and learning God's Word, the Bible, you are like a solider putting on your armor. Knowing God's Word will help you fight against sin and be strong for God.

God has given you armor to wear in your fight against Satan. Color the picture below that shows the armor you have been given.

breastplate (righteousness)

shield (faith)

sword (Bible)

Pray

Thank God for His Word and ask Him to help you remember it so you can be strong for Him.

SATURDAY Ephesians 6:18

You can pray everywhere, for everything, and ask God for anything. God wants you to do that. He also wants you to pray for other Christians.

Complete the crossword puzzle.

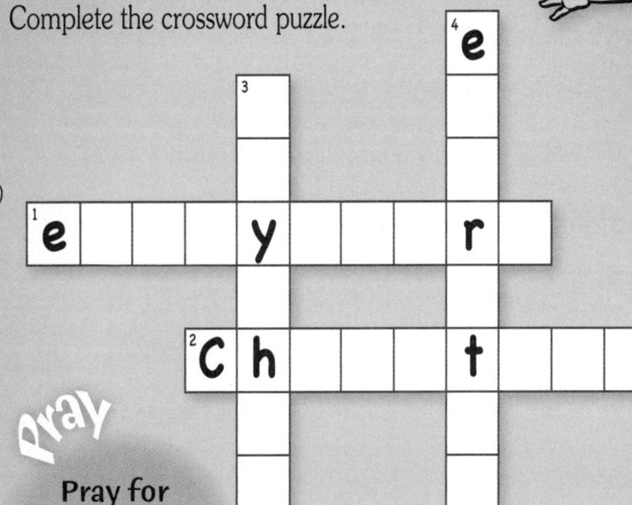

Pray

Pray for your friends who believe in Jesus.

COMMENT CORNER

Parent or Leader, circle a comment and/or write your own.

You're special · You can do it · God loves you! · Nice job! · We're proud of you! · Keep it up · WOW!

DAYS COMPLETED

To Word of Life Olympians

The following chart applies to all Word of Life Quiet Times
so that all ages will be on the same passage each day.

week 1	Aug 27 - Sep 2	Psalms 104:1-105:45
week 2	Sep 3 - Sep 9	Psalms 106:1-108:13
week 3	Sep 10 - Sep 16	Psalms 114:1-119:8
week 4	Sep 17 - Sep 23	Psalms 119:9-119:72
week 5	Sep 24 - Sep 30	Psalms 119:81-119:176
week 6	Oct 1 - Oct 7	Philippians 1:1-2:23
week 7	Oct 8 - Oct 14	Philippians 2:24-4:23
week 8	Oct 15 - Oct 21	Exodus 1:1-4:17
week 9	Oct 22 - Oct 28	Exodus 4:18-8:15
week 10	Oct 29 - Nov 4	Exodus 8:16-11:10
week 11	Nov 5 - Nov 11	Exodus 12:1-14:14
week 12	Nov 12 - Nov 18	Exodus 14:15-17:16
week 13	Nov 19 - Nov 25	Exodus 19:1-32:6
week 14	Nov 26 - Dec 2	Exodus 32:7-40:38
week 15	Dec 3 - Dec 9	2 Timothy 1:1-2:26
week 16	Dec 10 - Dec 16	2 Timothy 3:1-4:22
week 17	Dec 17 - Dec 23	Nahum 1:1-Malachi 4:6
week 18	Dec 24 - Dec 30	John 1:1-1:51
week 19	Dec 31 - Jan 6	John 2:1-4:15
week 20	Jan 7 - Jan 13	John 4:16-5:47
week 21	Jan 14 - Jan 20	John 6:1-6:71
week 22	Jan 21 - Jan 27	John 7:1-8:20
week 23	Jan 28 - Feb 3	John 8:21-9:34
week 24	Feb 4 - Feb 10	John 9:35-11:29
week 25	Feb 11 - Feb 17	John 11:30-12:43
week 26	Feb 18 - Feb 24	John 12:44-14:14

week 27	Feb 25 - Mar 3	John 14:15-16:33
week 28	Mar 4 - Mar 10	John 17:1-19:22
week 29	Mar 11 - Mar 17	John 19:23-21:25
week 30	Mar 18 - Mar 24	Romans 1:1-3:20
week 31	Mar 25 - Mar 31	Romans 3:21-6:23
week 32	Apr 1 - Apr 7	Romans 7:1-9:33
week 33	Apr 8 - Apr 14	Romans 10:1-12:21
week 34	Apr 15 - Apr 21	Romans 13:1-16:27
week 35	Apr 22 - Apr 28	Ezekiel 1:1-37:14
week 36	Apr 29 - May 5	Ezekiel 37:15-47:12
week 37	May 6 - May 12	Revelation 6:1-13:18
week 38	May 13 - May 19	Revelation 14:1-17:18
week 39	May 20 - May 26	Revelation 19:1-22:21
week 40	May 27 - June 2	Job 1:1-13:18
week 41	Jun 3 - Jun 9	Job 14:1-42:17
week 42	Jun 10- Jun 16	1 Peter 1:1-3:7
week 43	Jun 17 - Jun 23	1 Peter 3:8-5:14
week 44	Jun 24 - Jun 30	1 Kings 1:15-11:13
week 45	Jul 1 - Jul 7	1 Kings 11:41-18:16
week 46	Jul 8 - Jul 14	1 Kings 18:17-22:40
week 47	Jul 15 - Jul 21	2 Kings 1:1-5:16
week 48	Jul 22 - Jul 28	2 Kings 5:17-9:37
week 49	Jul 29- Aug 4	2 Kings 13:14-23:3
week 50	Aug 5 - Aug 11	Ephesians 1:1-2:22
week 51	Aug 12 - Aug 18	Ephesians 3:1-4:32
week 52	Aug 19 - Aug 25	Ephesians 5:1-6:24

Challenger

Scripture Memory

Check each verse as it is memorized.

Can I hide anything from God?

1

Psalm 69:5

O God, thou knowest my foolishness;
And my sins are not hid from thee.

How can I come to God?

2

John 14:6

Jesus saith unto him, I am the way, the truth, and the life: no man cometh unto the Father, but by me.

What must I do to walk in Christ?

3

Colossians 2:6

As ye have therefore received Christ Jesus the Lord, so walk ye in him.

How can I find God?

4

Proverbs 8:17

I love them that love me; And those that seek me early shall find me.

What will happen to my enemies when I please God first?

5

Proverbs 16:7

When a man's ways please the LORD, He maketh even his enemies to be at peace with him.

What keeps me from sin?

6

Psalm 119:11

Thy word have I hid in mine heart, That I might not sin against thee.

(This Quiet Time contains scripture memory verses in five translations. You may remove any sheets that are not needed.)

KJV

• Genesis • Exodus • Leviticus • Numbers • Deuteronomy • Joshua • Judges • Ruth • 1 Samuel •

2 Samuel • 1 Kings • 2 Kings • 1 Chronicles • 2 Chronicles • Ezra • Nehemiah • Esther • Job • Psalms • Proverbs • Ecclesiastes • Song of Solomon • Isaiah • Jeremiah • Lamentations • Ezekiel • Daniel •

•Hosea • Joel • Amos • Obadiah • Jonah • Micah • Nahum • Habakkuk • Zephaniah • Haggai • Zechariah • Malachi •

Challenge

What should I know that God can do?

7

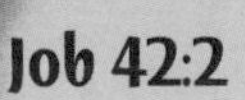

Job 42:2

I know that thou canst do every thing, And that no thought can be withholden from thee.

Why shouldn't I be proud?

8

Proverbs 16:18

Pride goeth before destruction,
And an haughty spirit before a fall.

What shows people that I am a Christian?

9

John 13:35

By this shall all men know that ye are my disciples, if ye have love one to another.

What should I not grow weary in doing?

10

2 Thessalonians 3:13

But ye, brethren, be not weary in well doing.

God can deliver me from what?

11

Psalm 120:2

Deliver my soul, O LORD, from lying lips, and from a deceitful tongue.

How will memorizing God's Word help me?

12

Psalm 37:31

The law of his God is in his heart; none of his steps shall slide.

• Matthew • Mark • Luke • John • Acts • Romans • 1 Corinthians • 2 Corinthians • Galatians • Ephesians •

Philippians • Colossians • 1 Thessalonians • 2 Thessalonians • 1 Timothy • 2 Timothy • Titus

• Philemon • Hebrews • James • 1 Peter • 2 Peter • 1 John • 2 John • 3 John • Jude • Revelation •

Challenger

Scripture Memory

Check each verse as it is memorized.

Can I hide anything from God?

1

Psalm 69:5

O God, You know my foolishness;
And my sins are not hidden from You.

How can I come to God?

2

John 14:6

Jesus said to him, I am the way, the truth, and the life.
No one comes to the Father except through Me.

What must I do to walk in Christ?

3

Colossians 2:6

As you therefore have received Christ Jesus the Lord,
so walk in Him.

How can I find God?

4

Proverbs 8:17

I love those who love me, And those
who seek me diligently will find me.

What will happen to my enemies when I please God first?

5

Proverbs 16:7

When a man's ways please the LORD, He makes
even his enemies to be at peace with him.

What keeps me from sin?

6

Psalm 119:11

Your word I have hidden in my heart,
That I might not sin against You.

(This Quiet Time contains scripture memory verses in five translations.
You may remove any sheets that are not needed.)

NKJV

• Genesis • Exodus • Leviticus • Numbers • Deuteronomy • Joshua • Judges • Ruth • 1 Samuel • 2 Samuel • 1 Kings • 2 Kings • 1 Chronicles • 2 Chronicles • Ezra • Nehemiah • Esther • Job • Psalms • Proverbs • Ecclesiastes • Song of Solomon • Isaiah • Jeremiah • Lamentations • Ezekiel • Daniel • Hosea • Joel • Amos • Obadiah • Jonah • Micah • Nahum • Habakkuk • Zephaniah • Haggai • Zechariah • Malachi •

Challenger

What should I know that God can do?

7

Job 42:2

I know that You can do everything, And that no purpose of Yours can be withheld from You.

Why shouldn't I be proud?

8

Proverbs 16:18

Pride goes before destruction,
And a haughty spirit before a fall.

What shows people that I am a Christian?

9

John 13:35

By this all will know that you are My disciples, if you have love for one another.

What should I not grow weary in doing?

10

2 Thessalonians 3:13

But as for you, brethren,
do not grow weary in doing good.

God can deliver me from what?

11

Psalm 120:2

Deliver my soul, O LORD, from lying lips
And from a deceitful tongue.

How will memorizing God's Word help me?

12

Psalm 37:31

The law of his God is in his heart;
none of his steps shall slide.

• Matthew • Mark • Luke • John • Acts • Romans • 1 Corinthians • 2 Corinthians • Galatians • Ephesians •
Philippians • Colossians • 1 Thessalonians • 2 Thessalonians • 1 Timothy • 2 Timothy • Titus
• Philemon • Hebrews • James • 1 Peter • 2 Peter • 1 John • 2 John • 3 John • Jude • Revelation •

Challenger

Scripture Memory

Check each verse as it is memorized.

Can I hide anything from God?

1

Psalm 69:5

O God, it is You who knows my folly,
And my wrongs are not hidden from You.

How can I come to God?

2

John 14:6

Jesus said to him, I am the way, and the truth, and the life;
no one comes to the Father but through Me.

What must I do to walk in Christ?

3

Colossians 2:6

Therefore as you have received Christ Jesus the Lord,
so walk in Him.

How can I find God?

4

Proverbs 8:17

I love those who love me; And
those who diligently seek me will find me.

What will happen to my enemies when I please God first?

5

Proverbs 16:7

When a man's ways are pleasing to the LORD, He
makes even his enemies to be at peace with him.

What keeps me from sin?

6

Psalm 119:11

Your word I have treasured in my heart,
That I may not sin against You.

(This Quiet Time contains scripture memory verses in five translations. You may remove any sheets that are not needed.)

NASB

• Genesis • Exodus • Leviticus • Numbers • Deuteronomy • Joshua • Judges • Ruth • 1 Samuel •

2 Samuel • 1 Kings • 2 Kings • 1 Chronicles • 2 Chronicles • Ezra • Nehemiah • Esther • Job • Psalms
• Proverbs • Ecclesiastes • Song of Solomon • Isaiah • Jeremiah • Lamentations • Ezekiel • Daniel •

•Hosea • Joel • Amos • Obadiah • Jonah • Micah • Nahum • Habakkuk • Zephaniah • Haggai • Zechariah • Malachi •

Challenge

What should I know that God can do?

Job 42:2

I know that You can do all things, And that
no purpose of Yours can be thwarted.

Why shouldn't I be proud?

8

Proverbs 16:18

Pride goes before destruction,
And a haughty spirit before stumbling.

What shows people that I am a Christian?

9

John 13:35

By this all men will know that you are My disciples,
if you have love for one another.

What should I not grow weary in doing?

10

2 Thessalonians 3:13

But as for you, brethren,
do not grow weary of doing good.

God can deliver me from what?

11

Psalm 120:2

Deliver my soul, O LORD, from lying lips,
From a deceitful tongue.

How will memorizing God's Word help me?

12

Psalm 37:31

The law of his God is in his heart;
His steps do not slip.

• Matthew • Mark • Luke • John • Acts • Romans • 1 Corinthians • 2 Corinthians • Galatians • Ephesians • Philippians • Colossians • 1 Thessalonians • 2 Thessalonians • 1 Timothy • 2 Timothy • Titus • Philemon • Hebrews • James • 1 Peter • 2 Peter • 1 John • 2 John • 3 John • Jude • Revelation •

Challenger

Scripture Memory

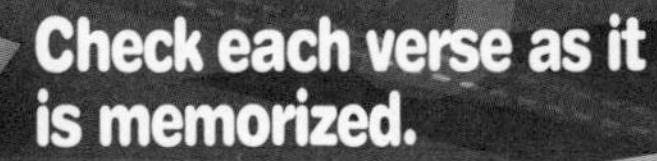

Check each verse as it is memorized.

Can I hide anything from God?

1

Psalm 69:5

You know my folly, O God;
my guilt is not hidden from you.

How can I come to God?

2

John 14:6

Jesus answered, I am the way and the truth and the life.
No one comes to the Father except through me.

What must I do to walk in Christ?

3

Colossians 2:6

So then, just as you received Christ Jesus as Lord,
continue to live in him.

How can I find God?

4

Proverbs 8:17

I love those who love me,
and those who seek me find me.

What will happen to my enemies when I please God first?

5

Proverbs 16:7

When a man's ways are pleasing to the LORD, he
makes even his enemies live at peace with him.

What keeps me from sin?

6

Psalm 119:11

I have hidden your word in my heart
that I might not sin against you.

(This Quiet Time contains scripture memory verses in five translations.
You may remove any sheets that are not needed.)

NIV

• Genesis • Exodus • Leviticus • Numbers • Deuteronomy • Joshua • Judges • Ruth • 1 Samuel • 2 Samuel • 1 Kings • 2 Kings • 1 Chronicles • 2 Chronicles • Ezra • Nehemiah • Esther • Job • Psalms • Proverbs • Ecclesiastes • Song of Solomon • Isaiah • Jeremiah • Lamentations • Ezekiel • Daniel • Hosea • Joel • Amos • Obadiah • Jonah • Micah • Nahum • Habakkuk • Zephaniah • Haggai • Zechariah • Malachi •

Challenge

What should I know that God can do?

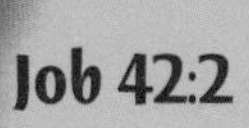

7

Job 42:2

I know that you can do all things;
no plan of yours can be thwarted.

Why shouldn't I be proud?

8

Proverbs 16:18

Pride goes before destruction,
a haughty spirit before a fall.

What shows people that I am a Christian?

9

John 13:35

By this all men will know that you are my disciples,
if you love one another.

What should I not grow weary in doing?

10

2 Thessalonians 3:13

And as for you, brothers,
never tire of doing what is right.

God can deliver me from what?

11

Psalm 120:2

Save me, O LORD, from lying lips
and from deceitful tongues.

How will memorizing God's Word help me?

12

Psalm 37:31

The law of his God is in his heart;
his feet do not slip.

• Matthew • Mark • Luke • John • Acts • Romans • 1 Corinthians • 2 Corinthians • Galatians • Ephesians •

Philippians • Colossians • 1 Thessalonians • 2 Thessalonians • 1 Timothy • 2 Timothy • Titus

• Philemon • Hebrews • James • 1 Peter • 2 Peter • 1 John • 2 John • 3 John • Jude • Revelation •

Challenger

Scripture Memory

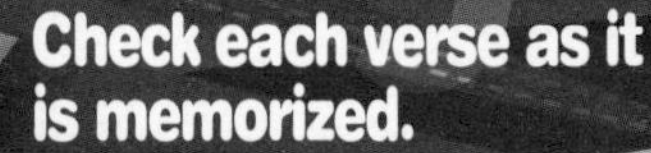

Check each verse as it is memorized.

Can I hide anything from God?

1

Psalm 69:5

O God, you know my folly; the wrongs I have done are not hidden from you.

How can I come to God?

2

John 14:6

Jesus said to him, I am the way, and the truth, and the life. No one comes to the Father except through me.

What must I do to walk in Christ?

3

Colossians 2:6

Therefore, as you received Christ Jesus the Lord, so walk in him.

How can I find God?

4

Proverbs 8:17

I love those who love me, and those who seek me diligently find me.

What will happen to my enemies when I please God first?

5

Proverbs 16:7

When a man's ways please the LORD, he makes even his enemies to be at peace with him.

What keeps me from sin?

6

Psalm 119:11

I have stored up your word in my heart, that I might not sin against you.

(This Quiet Time contains scripture memory verses in five translations. You may remove any sheets that are not needed.)

ESV

• Genesis • Exodus • Leviticus • Numbers • Deuteronomy • Joshua • Judges • Ruth • 1 Samuel • 2 Samuel • 1 Kings • 2 Kings • 1 Chronicles • 2 Chronicles • Ezra • Nehemiah • Esther • Job • Psalms • Proverbs • Ecclesiastes • Song of Solomon • Isaiah • Jeremiah • Lamentations • Ezekiel • Daniel • Hosea • Joel • Amos • Obadiah • Jonah • Micah • Nahum • Habakkuk • Zephaniah • Haggai • Zechariah • Malachi •

Challenge

What should I know that God can do?

7

Job 42:2

I know that you can do all things, and that no purpose of yours can be thwarted.

Why shouldn't I be proud?

8

Proverbs 16:18

Pride goes before destruction, and a haughty spirit before a fall.

What shows people that I am a Christian?

9

John 13:35

By this all people will know that you are my disciples, if you have love for one another.

What should I not grow weary in doing?

10

2 Thessalonians 3:13

As for you, brothers, do not grow weary in doing good.

God can deliver me from what?

11

Psalm 120:2

Deliver me, O LORD, from lying lips, from a deceitful tongue.

How will memorizing God's Word help me?

12

Psalm 37:31

The law of his God is in his heart; his steps do not slip.

• Matthew • Mark • Luke • John • Acts • Romans • 1 Corinthians • 2 Corinthians • Galatians • Ephesians •

Philippians • Colossians • 1 Thessalonians • 2 Thessalonians • 1 Timothy • 2 Timothy • Titus

• Philemon • Hebrews • James • 1 Peter • 2 Peter • 1 John • 2 John • 3 John • Jude • Revelation •